Second Edition   Dave Martin

Communicating Skills

A Language Arts Program

Over 50% recycled paper
including 10% post
consumer fibre

Plus de 50 p. 100 de
papier recyclé dont 10 p.
100 de fibres
post-consommation

» An official mark of Environment Canada
» Marque officielle d'Environnement Canada

HEATH

Table of Contents — An Overview

Unit 1

Working with Groups

Last spring, Ann and Linda decided to coach a softball team for children aged nine and ten. Imagine their surprise when forty excited players turned up for the first practice! Because the girls had too many people for one team, they decided to divide them into two groups.

A. Ann and Linda's players could be grouped in many different ways. How would you suggest they organize the teams? Here are two ways. See if you can think of three more possibilities.

1. _nine-year-olds, ten-year-olds_
2. _boys and girls_
3. _____
4. _____
5. _____

B. Arranging information or things in groups according to a plan is called **classifying**. Suggest a way to classify each of the following things. You may decide to classify some into more than two groups.

Example:

the vehicles in a parking lot

cars, trucks

1. the fans at a baseball game

_____

2. the fish in an aquarium

_____

3. the records in a record store

_____

To help people find information quickly and easily, librarians use the Dewey Decimal System to organize materials. In this system, information on athletics, outdoor sports and games is filed under the general numerical heading 796.

Because sports is such a large topic, materials on specific activities must be grouped. Books about games that use balls, for example, are filed under 796.3. Books on combat sports, such as boxing, are placed in 796.8. You'll find ice and snow sports under 796.9.

C. Imagine you work in a library and have been asked to file books on the following topics.

baseball hockey wrestling skiing polo bobsledding
squash judo curling lacrosse karate fencing

Use this chart to show how you would organize or classify the books. Check the definition of those sports you are not familiar with in the dictionary.

796.3	**796.8**	**796.9**

D. Each sport has its own set of terms. If you're interested in football, for example, you know about field goals, touchdowns, and conversions. If you're a figure skater, you may have tried a salchow, an axel, or a lutz. Read the following list of sports words. In which three sports might these words be used?

shortstop puck dribbling high-sticking bunt jump ball hat-trick sideline
infield rink diamond backboard lay-up power play double play free throw
home run face-off strikeout rebound slapshot sticks court dugout

Write the names of the three sports you've selected at the top of the columns in the following chart. Then classify the words, in the list above, by writing them under the correct heading.

Nouns are Naming Words

Did you know that words could also be classified? Words that name people, places, or things are classified as **nouns**. Most nouns stand for things you can actually see, touch, and hear such as: an *astronaut*, *Wayne Gretzky*, the *drugstore*, *Banff National Park*, a *sandwich*, and *waterfall*. Other nouns, such as *courage* and *patience*, represent ideas and feelings. Let's look at some examples:

People: my *sister*, *Randy*, *Mrs. Dickson*, the new *dentist*, my *uncle*

Places: *Vancouver Island*, *Toronto*, a large *city*, a new *building*

Things: a *hamburger*, some ripe *strawberries*, a red *petunia*, seven *coyotes*

Ideas: *freedom*, *honesty*, *liberty*, *hope*, *democracy*, *fairness*

Feelings: *love*, *fear*, *sadness*, *sorrow*, *joy*, *happiness*, *kindness*

Sometimes a noun may contain more than one word. *Red River cart*, for example, is one noun.

E. Circle the nouns in the following sentences. The number in parentheses tells you how many nouns there are in each sentence.

1. Near the stadium, the police found the abandoned car. (3)

2. Tarantulas, the largest spiders in the world, live in the jungles of South America. (5)

3. The dog buried the bone under the shrub near the fence. (4)

4. Audrey flew to Fredericton, New Brunswick, on Thursday. (4)

5. Artists in ancient Greece used pictures of dolphins to decorate coins, pottery, and

    walls. (7)

6. Frank decided to tell his father the truth about the missing money. (4)

7. The players on the bench cheered when Ellen scored the winning goal. (4)

8. The watchmaker took pride in his work. (3)

F. Add six nouns to each of the following lists.

1. Things you might find on a car, such as *tires*, *steering wheel*, *radio*

_____

2. Things you can hear, such as *thunder*, *cheering*, *whistling*

_____

3. Places you would like to visit, such as *Niagara Falls*, *Dawson City*, *Mediterranean Sea*

_____

4. Qualities you like in your friends, such as *kindness*, *friendliness*, *thoughtfulness*

_____

Sometimes nouns name a group or collection of persons or things. For example:

The *flock* of geese landed in the marsh.

The *committee* decided to meet Thursday after school.

The *team* practises in the gymnasium after school.

A noun used as the name of a group is called a **collective noun**. *Flock*, *committee*, and *team* are examples of collective nouns.

G. Each of the following italicized words is a collective noun. On the blank following the noun, tell what is in each group. If you're not sure what some of the nouns mean, check your dictionary. In your notebook, use each collective noun in an interesting sentence.

Example:

a *school* of *fish* _____

1. a *fleet* of _____   5. a *pack* of _____

2. a *swarm* of _____   6. a *gaggle* of _____

3. a *squadron* of _____   7. a *warren* of _____

4. a *pride* of _____   8. a *pod* of _____

H. To be a good writer, you must choose your nouns carefully. The words *crowd*, *mob*, and *rabble* all mean "a large number of people gathered together." Check the exact meaning of each of these words in a dictionary. Then use each one in a different sentence.

_____

_____

_____

_____

_____

_____

_____

I. Write five sentences in your notebook using collective nouns of your choice.

Sharpening Sentence Sense

A **sentence** is a group of words that makes sense by itself. It always begins with a capital and ends with a period, question mark, or exclamation mark.

J. Read each of the following word groups. If the group forms a sentence, write "S" in the blank at the left and add a period. If the word group does not form a sentence, write "NS."

_____ 1. My cousins from Montreal arrived Tuesday

_____ 2. Although the game started on time

_____ 3. Nobody answered

_____ 4. As soon as the ambulance reached the highway

_____ 5. The white horse standing beside the fence

_____ 6. You'll find the keys on the shelf

_____ 7. Before the game started

_____ 8. Walk slowly

_____ 9. Inside the old cabin we found a porcupine

_____ 10. While my father tried to repair the kitchen sink

You should have found five word groups that were not sentences. Add information to each of these groups to make them into interesting sentences. Write your new sentences in your notebook.

Unit 2

Two Kinds of Nouns

Nouns can be sorted or classified into two groups. Words such as *Jennifer, Ottawa, Elm Street,* and *Edmonton Oilers* are called proper nouns. A **proper noun** is a name for a specific person, place, or thing. Notice that a proper noun always starts with a capital letter.

Nouns such as *girl, city, street,* and *team* are called common nouns. **Common nouns** can name any person, place, or thing. They are capitalized only when they're the first word in a sentence.

A. Write a proper noun for each of these common nouns. Then, in your notebook, write a sentence using each of your proper nouns.

Example:

month *April*

1. holiday _____
2. continent _____
3. movie _____
4. river _____
5. author _____

6. planet _____
7. restaurant _____
8. nationality _____
9. prime minister _____
10. musician _____

Learning About Capital Letters

Each of the following types of proper nouns must start with a capital letter.

1 The names of towns, cities, provinces, territories, countries, and continents, such as:

Whitehorse, Halifax, New Brunswick, India, Africa

2. The name of a person or a pet, such as:

   Christy, Allan, Terry Fox, Pepper, Smoky

3. The title of a person, such as:

   Mrs. Chow, Professor Winston, Doctor Husvig, Sergeant Collins

4. The names of streets, avenues, boulevards, roads, and highways, such as:

   Howe Street, Tenth Avenue, Ross Road, Trans Canada Highway

5. The names of rivers, lakes, oceans, and mountains, such as:

   Athabasca River, Lake Ontario, Arctic Ocean, Mount Logan

6. The names of schools, buildings, bridges, and parks, such as:

   Glenwood School, Grandview Motel, Lion's Gate Bridge, Broadway Park

7. The names of days, months, and holidays, such as:

   Thursday, April, Mother's Day, Easter, New Year's Day

   The names of the seasons (spring, summer, fall, and winter) are not capitalized.

B. Proofreading means reading to find and correct mistakes in capitalization, punctuation, and spelling. Writers often use symbols to mark the needed changes. Read each of these sentences carefully. Draw three short lines under each letter that should be capitalized (a̲). The number in parentheses shows how many capitals are required.

1. The next game will be played on thanksgiving day at wilton park on oliver road. (6)
2. Last spring, the band from gladstone school in vancouver travelled to hamilton, ontario. (5)
3. In august, uncle george moved to waldeck, a small town near swift current, saskatchewan. (7)
4. The queen charlotte islands are in the pacific ocean off the coast of british columbia. (7)
5. Last winter, my aunt worked tuesdays and wednesdays at lakeview school on barclay drive. (6)
6. On friday professor chan from the university of new brunswick spoke at kirkland school. (8)
7. In july aunt susan and my father drove from montreal to summerside, prince edward island. (8)
8. On the flight from winnipeg to london, our plane refuelled at gander airport in newfoundland. (5)

Using Exact Nouns

Exact nouns add life to your work and give the reader a vivid picture of what you're describing. Too many general nouns can make your writing dull and uninteresting. Notice the difference in the following sentences.

   The man gave us a container of fruit.

   The farmer gave us a bag full of mangoes, papayas, and pineapples.

The second sentence is more interesting because it uses exact nouns. It helps the reader visualize what the writer is describing.

   On page 8 you'll find a paragraph from Marguerite Henry's novel *King of the Wind*. In this passage, she tells how Agba, a young Moroccan stableboy, races into the city looking for help for his sick colt. As you read the paragraph, notice how the author uses exact nouns to make the scene come alive.

Out the gates, down the hill to the city of Meknes he ran, past corn mills, past camels browsing before the tents of Arabs, past mules laden with crates of screaming chickens, past shepherds leading their flocks to market - down into the dark, crooked streets of the city. ...He flew past the shops - the scriveners, the meat-fryers, the shoemakers, the waxchandlers. ...On and on he went, weaving his way between street jugglers, snake charmers, water carriers, and small boys scurrying about with great trays of bread. He was trying to run away from trouble, but it hugged him like his own shadow.

Marguerite Henry, *King of the Wind*

C. Circle the specific nouns in the paragraph that helped you picture the city of Meknes.

D. Write at least three exact nouns for each of the following general nouns.
   Example:
   insect   *fly, beetle, ant, bee, wasp*

   1. bird   _____

   2. flower   _____

   3. tree   _____

   4. boat   _____

   5. machine   _____

   6. meat   _____

   7. metal   _____

   8. storm   _____

   9. rodent   _____

   10. animal   _____

Correcting Run-Together Sentences

When someone is talking, it is usually easy to tell where each sentence ends. The speaker's voice may drop, or the speaker may pause briefly.

When you are writing, you must mark the end of a sentence with a period, a question mark, or an exclamation mark. Always start each new sentence with a capital letter.

A **run-together** is composed of two or more sentences written as one sentence. Run-togethers are difficult to understand, because the reader is not shown where one sentence ends and the next one begins. Let's look at an example.

> The Pacific is the world's largest ocean covering more than one-third of the earth's surface so that if all the world's continents were put in the Pacific, there would still be room for another continent the size of Asia.

You can correct run-togethers by dividing them into separate sentences.

> The Pacific is the world's largest ocean covering more than one-third of the earth's surface. If all the world's continents were put in the Pacific, there would still be room for another continent the size of Asia.

E. Rewrite each of the following word groups in your notebook. Add capital letters and punctuation where needed.

1. have you heard the news our team won the city championship

2. walk to the front of the room and take a deep breath then start speaking

3. my mother likes to knit she just finished making me a sweater

4. just then we saw tony crawling up his arm was a large spider

5. why did you drop that box was it too heavy

6. we flew to winnipeg then we took a bus to portage la prairie

F. Choose five of the following topics. In your notebook, write two interesting sentences about each of the topics you select.

1. a television program	5. a musical instrument	9. a concert
2. a favorite dessert	6. a building	10. a nightmare
3. a relative	7. a downtown street	11. a hobby
4. an unusual car	8. a doctor's waiting room	12. a pet

G. The following paragraph is difficult to understand because it is a run-together sentence. Rewrite the paragraph in your notebook, dividing it into sentences.

> No one knows exactly how many islands there are in the Pacific geographers estimate there are at least twenty thousand but there may be more than thirty thousand a few of these islands such as New Guinea, the second largest island in the world, are quite large but many are only a few square kilometres in size in fact, all of them together cover less area than does the province of Quebec

Unit 3

The Dictionary: Finding Your Way Around

A dictionary is an important reference book. It not only tells you what words mean, but also gives you useful information about them. To get the most out of your dictionary, you should learn how to find information quickly.

To use a dictionary well you must know the alphabet forward and backward. Putting words in alphabetical order is quite easy if they all begin with different letters. The job is harder, however, when they all start with the same letter. Then you must use the letters within the word to work out the correct order.

A. Rewrite each of the following groups of words in alphabetical order.

Example:

glance   garage   grass   goldfish   gulp   ginger

garage, ginger, glance, goldfish, grass, gulp

1. trap   forest   shadow   rugby   unhook   dinosaur

2. laundry   nozzle   hawk   marigold   onion   kettle

3. thistle   quail   umbrella   slippery   vibrate   remember

4. alarm   astronaut   absent   author   army   accept   African

5. glitter   gravy   general   gummy   garlic   gym   giraffe

6. steam   stove   strangle   station   stitch   stuffy

7. coast   compass   college   coffee   confess   cocoa   coin

8. restrict   resort   rescue   resign   resume   restaurant   respect

9. planet plant plank plantation plane planner planetarium

10. thresh threaten three threw thread threat

Further Uses of Capital Letters

Here are some more proper nouns that must start with capital letters.

1 The names of clubs and organizations, such as:

Rotary Club, Red Cross, Girl Guides, Saskatchewan Roughriders, National Hockey League

2 The names of airplanes, ships, trains, airlines, and railways, such as:

Boeing 747, Flying Cloud, Thunderbird
Airlines, Canadian National Railway

3 The names of languages and nationalities, such as:

English, French, German, Chinese,
Hindi, Russian

4 The names of periods and events in history, such as:

Middle Ages, Battle of Quebec, Second
World War, Expo 86

5 The names of stars, planets, satellites, and constellations, such as:

North Star, Venus, Mars, Anik,
Big Dipper

(The words *sun*, *earth*, and *moon* are usually not capitalized.)

6 The names of churches and religious groups, such as:

Collingwood United Church, Roman Catholic, Judaism, Hinduism, Buddhism

7 The names of school courses that deal with languages, such as:

Mrs. Anderson teaches social studies, science, and French.

8 The first word and all important words in the titles of books, poems, stories, songs, newspapers, magazines, movies, and television programs, such as:

Communicating Skills, Never Cry Wolf, Casey at the Bat, O Canada, Globe and Mail,
Maclean's, The Cosby Show

9 The words *north*, *south*, *east*, and *west* are not capitalized when they name directions.

When you reach the corner, turn south.

Direction words need capital letters, however, when they name parts of the country or of the world.

Most of the people who live in the Middle East are Arabs.

B. Proofread the following sentences to find words that need capitals. Draw three short lines under each letter that should be capitalized.

1. napoleon bonaparte, a french general, was defeated at the battle of waterloo on june 18, 1815.

2. my aunt is studying dentistry at dalhousie university in halifax.

3. the dunbar trojans practise tuesday and thursday evenings at milner school on hatfield avenue.

4. in 1853 donald mckay, a canadian shipbuilder, launched the great republic, the largest wooden ship ever built.

5. the players on the japanese basketball team flew to northern manitoba on maple leaf airlines.

6. the mackenzie, canada's longest river, begins in great slave lake and flows northwest to the beaufort sea.

7. the choir sang on christmas eve at holy family church on covington boulevard.

8. in june 1215, at runnymede, the english barons forced king john to sign the magna carta.

9. during the middle ages, a plague called the black death killed one-quarter of the people in europe.

10. the motion picture, *the miracle worker*, shows how anne sullivan taught helen keller to speak.

Singular and Plural Nouns

Nouns that name *only one* person, place, or thing are called **singular nouns**. Nouns that name *more than one* person, place, or thing are called **plural nouns**.

Singular	rabbit	apple	truck	goat
Plural	rabbits	apples	trucks	goats

Here are some tips to help you form the plural of most nouns.

1 Nouns ending in *s, x, z, ch,* and *sh* are hard to pronounce if only *s* is added. To make these nouns plural, add *es*.

glass - glasses	fox - foxes	waltz - waltzes
dish - dishes	bench - benches	leech - leeches

2 Nouns ending in *y* are made plural in one of two ways. If a vowel - *a, e, i, o,* or *u* - comes before the *y*, add *s*.

tray - trays	donkey - donkeys	boy - boys

If a consonant comes before the *y*, change the *y* to *i* and add *es*.

canary - canaries	city - cities	penny - pennies

3 To pluralize many nouns ending in *o*, add *s* to the singular form.

    radio - radios   cuckoo - cuckoos   piano - pianos

Some nouns ending in *o* are made plural by adding *es*.

    tomato - tomatoes   echo - echoes   potato - potatoes

A few nouns that end in *o* can be made plural by adding either *s* or *es*.

    volcano - volcanos *or* volcanoes   cargo - cargos *or* cargoes

4 Some singular nouns that end in *f* or *fe* are made plural by adding *s*.

    gulf - gulfs   handkerchief - handkerchiefs   giraffe - giraffes

To pluralize other singular nouns that end in *f* or *fe*, change the *f* or *fe* to *v* and add *es*.

    knife - knives   wife - wives   thief - thieves

The plurals of some nouns ending in *f* can be formed in either way.

    hoof - hoofs *or* hooves   wharf - wharfs *or* wharves

5 When some nouns become plural, the vowel sounds change, too.

    tooth - teeth   man - men   mouse - mice

6 Some nouns have the same form in the singular and the plural. Most of these are names of animals.

    trout   moose   salmon   elk

C. Write the plural of each of these nouns. Use a dictionary to check your answers.

Set 1

1. guppy _____
2. ranch _____
3. box _____
4. kangaroo _____
5. half _____
6. rodeo _____
7. jaw _____
8. foot _____
9. sky _____
10. piano _____
11. circus _____
12. woman _____
13. buffalo _____

Set 2

1. mattress _____
2. valley _____
3. navy _____
4. deer _____
5. zero _____
6. chief _____
7. discovery _____
8. ocean _____
9. monkey _____
10. leaf _____
11. worry _____
12. mouse _____
13. life _____

14. bush _____

15. holiday _____

16. wish _____

17. roof _____

18. jelly _____

19. potato _____

20. soprano _____

14. church _____

15. mystery _____

16. goose _____

17. army _____

18. hero _____

19. shelf _____

20. journey _____

Sorting Ideas into Paragraphs

Have you ever noticed how things are grouped in everyday life? The manager of a bookstore, for example, keeps all the books on computers in one place. In a supermarket, all the cereals are shelved in one area. Imagine how confused we would be if items were not kept in some kind of order.

To keep readers from being confused, writers arrange sentences into paragraphs. A **paragraph** is a group of sentences about one subject or idea. This idea is called the **main idea**. Some paragraphs have many sentences. Others have only a few. In a well-written paragraph, however, all the sentences will be about one main idea.

A paragraph always begins on a new line. The first word is usually moved in, or **indented**, from the margin, like the first word in this paragraph.

D. Suppose you have been studying ancient Egypt in class and have been asked to write a paragraph about the building of the Great Pyramid. Only four of the following details would be useful in such a paragraph. Cross out the three that don't belong. Be prepared to explain why you feel these details do not belong.

1. The Great Pyramid is built on a base that covers over five hectares, large enough to hold ten football fields.
2. The stones were towed on sledges up the sides of the pyramid on ramps of sand.
3. Thieves broke into most of the pyramids and stole gold and valuable artifacts.
4. Almost 2 500 000 blocks of stone were used in the Great Pyramid.
5. The ruins of thirty-five pyramids still stand near the Nile River in Egypt.
6. King Khufu was buried in the Great Pyramid.
7. The Great Pyramid took 100 000 laborers twenty years to build.

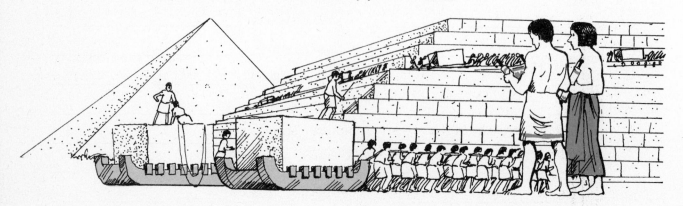

Unit 4

Understanding Guide Words

Two words, called **guide words**, appear at the top of each page in a dictionary. The one at the top left tells you the first word on the page. The one at the top right tells you the last word on the page.

When you're looking for a word in the dictionary, you should follow these guide words. Like signs on a highway, they tell you which way to turn to find the word you want.

A. Under each pair of guide words below is a group of five words. Circle the three that would appear on the same page as the given guide words.

Example:

giant - gill

(giggle) gilt (giddy) (gift) ghost

1. **loft - lonely**

   long   log   lodge   lollipop   logger

2. **tank - target**

   tango   tap   taping   tar   tasty

3. **foam - follow**

   folk   fond   food   fog   fold

4. **duel - dump**

   dull   dumb   dunce   dugout   due

5. **pack - page**

   packer   pace   pad   paddle   paint

6. **ring - rise**

   ringed   rip   rink   risk   rising

7. **dark - dawn**

   dare   date   dash   daub   daze

8. **male - mangle**

   mall   mail   man   mane   mango

9. **hot - house**

   how   hotel   hound   hourly   host

10. **still - stole**

    stolen   stoic   stir   stile   stilt

B. In your notebook, sort the following words into three lists. In the first list, put all the words found on the same dictionary page as the guide words *scrape* and *scroll*. In the second list, put the words found on a previous page. In the third list, put the words found on following pages. You should have five words in each list.

   scratch   scout   screech   scrub   scent   sculpture   school   scream

   search   scrap   seahorse   script   scrunch   scramble   screen

Verbs: Where the Action Is

Nouns are words that name persons, places, or things. **Verbs** are usually action words, like *swim, laugh, climb,* or *push.* They express what the nouns are doing.

> The owl *pounced* on the mouse.

> The four boys *jumped* the fence.

Sometimes verbs explain what's happening in someone's mind. Here is an example.

> My sister *memorized* the poem.

Some verbs express no action at all, as in these sentences.

> Ginny *is* my cousin from Red Deer.

> That truck *needs* new brakes.

C. Circle the verb in each of these sentences.

1. The ferry Sam McBride sails from Toronto to Centre Island.

2. The puppy crawled through the hole in the fence.

3. The frisky colts galloped across the field.

4. Yesterday our dog ate five hamburgers.

5. The helicopter flew over the volcano.

6. Those boys are often late.

7. Carol and Marie were the winners this year.

8. My uncle's summer cottage is on Lake Nipigon.

D. Think of a verb to go with each of the following nouns. The first two have been done for you. Be as imaginative as you can.

1. streams *gurgle*
2. mice *scamper*
3. scarecrows _____
4. dead fish _____
5. bubbles _____
6. motorcycles _____
7. clouds _____
8. snails _____

9. flames _____
10. dinosaurs _____
11. candles _____
12. hawks _____
13. balloons _____
14. babies _____
15. large trucks _____
16. football players _____

Using Verbs to Add Vitality

When good writers edit or revise their work, they often begin by looking carefully at their verbs. Always choose verbs that make your writing clear and exact.

Here, for example, is how Jim Kjelgaard describes the fight between his dog, Buck, and a mountain lion. Notice how the author uses strong, action-packed verbs to help the reader see exactly what's happening.

Buck twisted out of danger and bore in from the side, slicing at the lion's flank. His fangs ripped through skin into flesh. The lion slashed with a front paw, but where he had intended to deal the dog a crippling blow he succeeded only in knocking him sideways. When the lion tried to follow up and pin the hound down, Buck rolled out of the way. He scrambled to his feet and faced his enemy.

Jim Kjelgaard, *Lion Hound*

E. On the line under each of the following sentences, write at least three strong verbs to replace the weak verb in heavy type. Circle the verb you feel is most effective in each group. Then write your own interesting sentences in your notebook using the verbs you circled.

Example:

The mouse **ran** into its hole.

scrambled, darted, dashed, scampered, zipped, dove

1. The thieves **put** the money into a small suitcase.

_____

2. "Watch out for that truck," **said** the officer.

_____

3. The huge crocodile **went** into the water.

_____

4. In winter frogs **go** under the mud at the bottom of ponds.

_____

5. Suddenly thousands of bats **came** out of the cave.

_____

6. The wolf **fell** down the chimney.

_____

F. In your notebook, write an interesting sentence using each of the following verbs. You may use more than one verb in a sentence.

groaned cuffed snatched bellowed swaggered loped
jumbled clogged coaxed shuddered waddled whacked

Narrowing the Topic

A common mistake in writing paragraphs is choosing a topic that is too general. Before you start to write, decide if the subject you have chosen is suitable for a single paragraph. A topic such as "birds," for example, is too broad for a paragraph. With a general subject such as this, decide first what aspect of the overall topic you want to write about. This process is called **narrowing**, or limiting, the topic. Let's see how it works.

General topic:	birds
A specific group of birds:	birds of prey
A specific bird from this group:	the peregrine falcon
One activity of the peregrine:	how the peregrine falcon kills its prey

Having narrowed the topic, you could then write a paragraph such as the following.

   The combination of high speed and outstanding eyesight makes the peregrine falcon an exceptional hunter. Peregrines usually attack other birds by diving on them from above. In these dives they flash downward at speeds up to 280 km/h and strike their prey a deadly blow with a half-closed foot. Smaller birds are often seized in mid-air. If the victim is heavy, the falcon allows it to tumble to the ground and then lands beside it.

G. The following topics are too general to be handled in a single paragraph. Narrow each topic to one that is suitable for a paragraph of eight to ten sentences. Make sure each topic in a set is more specific than the one preceding it.

Example:

Winter sports

a. _skiing_

b. _ski-racing_

c. _my first cross-country race_

1. Building things   a. _____

                                           b. _____

                                           c. _____

2. Cooking   a. _____

                                           b. _____

                                           c. _____

3. Pollution   a. _____

                                           b. _____

                                           c. _____

4. Space travel   a. _____

                                           b. _____

                                           c. _____

5. Television programs   a. _____

                                           b. _____

                                           c. _____

6. Playing board games   a. _____

                                           b. _____

                                           c. _____

7. Family problems   a. _____

                                           b. _____

                                           c. _____

8. Babysitting   a. _____

                                           b. _____

                                           c. _____

H. Look back at the topics you wrote on line C in Exercise **G**. Choose one and write an interesting paragraph about it. Remember to use as many exact nouns and verbs as possible.

Unit 5

Subject and Predicate: An Essential Team

A group of words that makes sense by itself is called a **sentence**. Sometimes sentences are very short. A fire fighter, for example, could simply shout "Jump!" to someone trapped on the balcony of a burning hotel — and that would be a sentence.

Most sentences can be divided into two parts. The part that tells *who* or *what* the sentence is about is called the **subject**. The second part of the sentence, called the **predicate**, gives information about the subject or tells what the subject does. The predicate always contains a verb.

Subject: Who or what is the sentence about?	**Predicate:** What do we learn about the subject?
Our neighbor's dog	howled until after midnight.
The huge crocodile	slithered into the muddy water.
A cutlass	is a short, curved sword.

A. The subject is usually found at the beginning of a sentence. In each of the following sentences, draw one line under all the words in the subject. Draw two lines under all the words in the predicate. All words in the sentence must be underlined.

Example:

The nine planes screamed overhead.

1. The menacing shape crept slowly across the lawn.

2. The hungry crow perched on the window ledge.

3. Cindy and Lorraine won the badminton tournament.

4. A large herd of elk blocked the highway.

5. We raced through the park and across the bridge.

6. All the homes in the valley were destroyed in the forest fire.

7. The team from North Battleford won the championship.

8. Some of the largest trees on the island had been cut down.

9. The northern part of Manitoba has rich deposits of copper, gold, nickel, and zinc.

10. About two-thirds of the people in Montreal speak French.

Helping Verbs

Sometimes a verb is made up of more than one word. The verb parts that come before the main verb are called **helping verbs**. Here are two sentences that have a helping verb and a main verb.

Ken *will feed* the dog at about six o'clock.

My parents *are flying* to Calgary tonight.

Some sentences have two or three helping verbs before the main verb.

Your sister *must have eaten* my lunch.

You *should have been told* about the test.

Sometimes the helping verb and the main verb are separated by words that are not verbs.

Cindy *has* just *finished painting* the fence.

Tom *did* not *know* the answer.

Here is a list of the most common helping verbs.

am	was	be	has	do	must	can	will	shall
is	were	been	have	does	may	could	would	should
are			had	did	might			

B. In the following sentences, circle each main verb. Underline the helping verbs.

Example:

Your car <u>should</u> <u>be</u> (repaired) by six o'clock.

1. The cat must have been locked in the garage.

2. I will never forget that day.

3. My father has been working in the garden all day.

4. The team picture will not be taken until Tuesday.

5. We should probably have left earlier.

6. Terry could not find his notebook.

7. Those horses must have been running for a long time.

8. Tanya could not possibly have taken the key.

9. The old pirate had not found the trail to the cave.

10. My dog's leg could easily have been broken.

11. Did he walk all the way home?

12. Shouldn't you have told the principal about the phone call?

Using Commas with Addresses and Dates

1 When an address is part of a sentence, use commas to separate the city from the street. Commas must also be used to separate the province, state, or country from the rest of the sentence.

> Beth Tanaka's mail should be sent to 4643 Rymal Road East,
> Hamilton, Ontario L8W 1B6 until June 6.

2 With dates, separate the day of the month from the year with a comma. When a complete date is part of a sentence, separate the year from the rest of the sentence with a comma.

> On Thursday, August 27, 1987, my grandparents moved to Flin Flon.

> A comma is not needed if the date consists of the month and the year only.

> The expedition left for the Arctic in April 1906.

C. Add commas where necessary in the following sentences.

1. The trip from Tokyo Japan to Melbourne Australia took four months.

2. My parents were married on March 10 1975 in Springdale Newfoundland.

3. Alexander Graham Bell was born on March 3 1847 in Edinburgh Scotland.

4. Write to us at 2653 Mountain Road Moncton New Brunswick E1G 1B6 during the summer.

5. On Sunday July 20 1969 the Apollo 11 lunar module landed on the moon.

D. In your notebook, answer each of the following questions with a complete sentence. Be sure to put the commas in the correct places.

1. When were you born? (Include the day, month, and year.)

2. Where do you live? (Include the street, town or city, and province.)

3. What day, month, and year was last Thursday?

4. What city outside North America would you most like to visit? (Include the city and the country in your answer.)

5. Write a sentence telling when and where a famous person in history was born. (Use an encyclopedia to find the information.)

But How Do You Say It?

Once you have found a word, the dictionary tells you how it's pronounced. This information is usually given in brackets right after the entry word. Compare the respelling in the brackets with the words listed in the pronunciation key. The pronunciation key, usually found at the front of the dictionary, explains the symbols used in the definitions. A shortened form of this key is often printed on every second page.

E. In the box at the right is a pronunciation key from a dictionary. Use it to write the regular spelling of each of the following words.

> hat, āge, fär, let; ēqual, tėrm; it, īce
> hot, ōpen, ôrder; oil, out; cup, pùt, rüle
> əbove, takən, pencəl, leməm circəs
> ch, child; ng, long; sh, ship
> th, thin; ᵮH, then; zh, measure
> *Copyright © 1983, Gage Canadian Dictionary*

Example:

nīt ___*night*___

1. grōn _____
2. skēz _____
3. fīt _____
4. rān _____
5. kōkō _____

6. hûrē _____
7. jīənt _____
8. prīs _____
9. tėrkē _____
10. grēt _____

F. Use symbols from the pronunciation key, above, to rewrite the following words. When you finish, check your answers in the dictionary.

Example:

knee ___*nē*___

1. debt _____
2. ache _____
3. comb _____
4. rein _____
5. phone _____
6. knock _____
7. sigh _____

8. though _____
9. yew _____
10. corps _____
11. valet _____
12. subtle _____
13. mischievous _____
14. quay _____

The dictionary also shows how words are divided into syllables. Some syllables are pronounced with more force, or **stress**, than others. Dictionary writers use a heavy raised mark (′) to show a stressed syllable: ready (red′ ē).

G. Rewrite each of the following words leaving a space between the syllables. Mark the syllables that are stressed. Use a dictionary to check your work.

1. mammal _____   6. telephone _____

2. until _____   7. library _____

3. improve _____   8. grasshopper _____

4. power _____   9. skeleton _____

5. regular _____   10. impossible _____

H. Each of the words in this exercise can be pronounced in more than one way. Look up each word in your dictionary. Write the pronunciations on the line following each word, marking the stressed syllables as well. Circle the pronunciation you use most often.

Example:

arctic _ärk'tik, (är'tik)_ _____

1. missile _____

2. apricot _____

3. either _____

4. vase _____

5. schedule _____

I. Look up each of the following words in the dictionary. Notice that each word can be pronounced in two ways and that each pronunciation has a different meaning. On the line following each word, write the pronunciations, including stress marks, as you did for Exercise **H**. Then, in your notebook, write a sentence for each pronunciation showing the two ways the word could be used.

Example:

minute _min'it, mīnüt'_ _____

1. record _____

2. desert _____

3. present _____

4. permit _____

5. refuse _____

6. invalid _____

Topic Sentences as Signposts

In our national parks, rangers mark trails with signs like this, so hikers know exactly where each trail leads. Writers often use a sentence called a topic sentence in much the same way. **Topic sentences** tell the reader what a paragraph is about. The topic sentence usually appears at the beginning of a paragraph.

Read the following paragraph carefully. The topic sentence is printed in italics.

> *Modern industry could not exist without electricity.* Electric motors run drills, lathes, milling machines, and other tools. These tools mass-produce parts for products that are quickly assembled on electrically operated conveyor belts. Electricity melts and welds metals. It puts gold and silver plating on eyeglass frames, jewelry, tableware, and other objects. Powerful electric cranes lift huge loads. Delicate electronic instruments measure the thickness of steel with microscopic precision. Electricity runs elevators and escalators. ...Calculators, computers, electric typewriters, and photocopying machines enable office workers to save time and effort.
>
> Excerpted from *The World Book Encyclopedia.* © 1989 World Book, Inc.

J. The topic sentence tells us the paragraph will be about the importance of electricity to industry. List six examples the writer gives to prove that electricity is an important form of energy.

1. _____

2. _____

3. _____

4. _____

5. _____

6. _____

K. In your notebook, write an interesting topic sentence that you could use to begin a paragraph that:

1. Describes your best friend.

2. Urges the government to create a new school holiday in February.

3. Tells a visitor from a distant planet how to ride a bike.

4. Explains how you feel about homework.

5. Describes your feelings about smoking.

6. Tells about an embarrassing moment in your life.

7. Explains why you dislike a particular television commercial.

8. Describes the car of the future.

Unit 6

Editing: An Important Skill

Learning how to write also involves learning how to rewrite. Seldom do the words come out in the best order the first time. Professional writers often change or revise their work many times. They cross out words, add words, replace some words with others, and rearrange sentences and paragraphs. Revising a draft is called **editing**. Editing may involve changing *what* you said, *how* you said it, or both.

When you edit, look carefully at your words and sentences. Ask yourself, "Is this the best way to express these ideas to others?" While you're editing, be sure to make good use of your dictionary and thesaurus. These books will help you express your ideas more effectively.

Most experienced writers suggest you put your draft away for a few days before you try to edit it. After this "cooling off" period, you'll be able to see more clearly which changes are needed.

In this unit you'll practise editing topic sentences. A topic sentence must do more than simply let the reader know what the paragraph is about. An effective topic sentence also grabs the reader's attention.

Often, writers make the mistake of starting with a topic sentence that is too general, such as:

Training a dog is hard work.

This sentence leaves too many questions unanswered. What is the dog being trained to do? How much work is required? To improve the sentence, use specific words and ideas.

Housebreaking a puppy can be a frustrating experience.

The new sentence not only is more interesting, but also gives the reader a clearer idea of what the paragraph will be about.

A. Each of the following topic sentences is too general to be effective. Rewrite each sentence making it more exact. In each sentence, try to give the reader a clear idea of what the paragraph will be about.

1. I enjoy playing games.

_____

_____

2. Winter is the best season.

_____

_____

3. There are many ways to improve our school.

_____

_____

4. Learning to play a musical instrument is hard.

_____

_____

5. My sister (or brother) is a problem.

_____

_____

6. This year we had an interesting holiday.

_____

_____

_____

7. I do many things in my spare time.

_____

_____

8. The weather affects me a great deal.

_____

_____

Discovering Your Dictionary

The words listed in a dictionary in heavy type are called **entry words**. All the information given about a word is called the **entry**. If you were to look up the word *parrot* in the dictionary, for example, you would find an entry like the one at the right.

The entry word (**A**) gives you the correct spelling of the word. If the word is a proper noun, such as *French Canadian*, it will be capitalized. All other words start with small letters. The dot between the two "r's" shows how to divide the word into syllables. Right after the entry word is the respelling of the word (**B**), showing how it is pronounced.

This dictionary entry lists three definitions of the word *parrot*. Notice that one definition is followed by a sentence written in *italics* (**C**) showing how the word would be used with that meaning. The diagram at the right (**D**) illustrates Definition 1. This illustration gives you more information about the entry word. At the end of the entry (**E**), the dictionary points out that in Definitions 1 and 2 the word *parrot* is used as a noun. Definition 3 shows that the word can also be used as a verb.

Use your dictionary to do the exercises on page 28.

A   B
  \   / \
par·rot (par′ ət or per′ ət) **1** a bird of warm regions having a stout, hooked bill and, often, brightly colored feathers. Some parrots can imitate sounds and repeat words and sentences. **2** a person who repeats words   C or acts without understanding them. **3** repeat   / without understanding: *The small child parroted the words of the song.*   1, 2 *n.,* 3 *v.*

A grey parrot — about 30 cm long with the tail

B. Some of the following words need capital letters. Draw three short lines under the letters that should be capitalized.

science   french   big dipper   house of commons

south pole   maritimes   german measles klondike gold rush

canada goose   old testament   far east   celsius thermometer

C. Six of the following words are usually written as two separate words. Use the proofreading symbol for a space (a number sign and a caret, ⩔) to separate these words.

Example:

homerun
⩔

goodnight   quicksand   shortcut   snowfall

snowflake   blackbear   restroom   bullfrog

headstart   earache   bunkhouse   barndance

D. Dictionaries often give the plural forms of nouns in heavy type right after the respelling of the word or at the end of the entry. Use your dictionary to find the plural of each of these nouns.

1. tornado _____ 7. avocado _____

2. cactus _____   8. index _____

3. fungus _____   9. larva _____

4. banjo _____   10. mouthful _____

5. trout _____   11. mongoose _____

6. son-in-law _____ 12. formula _____

E. A dictionary can also give you the meaning of abbreviations. Look up each of these abbreviations in your dictionary. In the blanks write what each abbreviation stands for.

1. A.W.L. _____ 8. C.O.D. _____

2. CNIB _____   9. UNICEF _____

3. ICBM _____   10. MP _____

4. PQ _____   11. etc. _____

5. RN _____   12. CFB _____

6. biog. _____   13. Q.C. _____

7. e.g. _____   14. PDT _____

The Comma in a Series

Three or more similar things or events that happen one after the other are called a **series**. You will often see a number of similar words or phrases listed in a series. The following sentence, for example, lists a series of nouns.

Cormorants, kingfishers, herons, and *pelicans* often catch fish and other water animals.

In the following sentence, the words in the series are verbs.

Birds move about on land by *running, walking, hopping,* and *climbing.*

Sometimes a series is made up of groups of words or phrases.

The small bird *scooped up the water in its bill, tipped its head back,* and *let the water trickle down its throat.*

Notice how commas are used to separate the parts of the series in the sentences you have just read. A series of three items requires two commas. A series of four items requires three commas, and so on.

F. In each of these sentences, underline the words or word groups that form a series. Add commas where necessary.

1. Eagles hawks and owls often hunt mice for food.

2. The anhinga's sharp bill long neck and webbed feet help it catch fish.

3. Water birds feed on fish snails water weeds tiny shrimps and worms.

4. In summer birds mate lay their eggs and raise their families.

5. The crow lines its nest with grass strips of bark fine roots and moss.

6. Birds help farmers by eating weed seeds catching insect pests and killing rats and mice.

7. Goose feathers are often used to stuff pillows sleeping bags and mattresses.

8. Some birds, such as chickadees swallows woodpeckers and small owls live largely on insects.

9. Birds catch their food in the air on the ground inside flowers and trees and even in the mud.

Subject and Predicate: Changing the Position

The most common place for the subject is at the beginning of the sentence. When the subject comes before the verb, a sentence is said to be in **natural order**. Most sentences are in natural order, like this:

A large skunk sat right in the middle of our tent.

Always putting the subject first, however, is like having pizza for supper every day. All of us enjoy a change. To make your writing more interesting, try moving the subject from time to time. Sometimes you can put the subject after the predicate, like this:

Right in the middle of our tent sat *a large skunk.*

A sentence in which the verb, or any part of it, comes before the subject, is said to be in **inverted order.**

G. Rewrite each of these sentences moving the subject from the beginning to the end.

1. Many colorful wildflowers grew in the mountain meadows.

_____

2. Thick yellow smoke poured from the grain elevator.

_____

3. The mother grizzly raced straight toward the terrified hikers.

_____

H. The subject can sometimes be placed in the middle of the predicate. Underline the complete subject in each of these sentences.

Example:

After a six-day search, <u>the rescue team</u> found the missing hikers.

1. During the night, the wind drove the ship closer to the rocks.

2. After the rain, the spider's web sparkled like jewels.

3. In the last inning, our team scored six runs.

4. Before breakfast, I usually run five kilometres.

5. Near the lake, the trail is hard to follow.

6. Slowly and carefully the climbers worked their way across the glacier.

7. On Saturday my parents celebrated their fifteenth wedding anniversary.

8. To escape the forest fire, the moose waded out into the lake.

9. Last night, about eleven o'clock, the burglar alarm on our neighbor's house began ringing.

10. By the end of the summer, Carla had saved three hundred dollars.

I. Underline the subject in each of the following sentences. Then rewrite each sentence putting the subject in a different place.

Example:

The <u>paramedics</u> quickly loaded their gear into the rescue helicopter.

Quickly the paramedics loaded their gear into the rescue helicopter.

1. The thunder rumbled between the hills all night.

_____

_____

2. With a tremendous thud the huge fir tree crashed to the ground.

_____

_____

3. We found the remains of an old sawmill on the far side of the meadow.

_____

_____

4. Joanne watched the ground squirrels scurrying in and out of their burrows for almost an hour.

_____

_____

How Verbs Tell Time

Verbs are words that tell what is happening in the sentence. Usually they are action words, such as *swim, laugh, chop,* or *push.*

Verbs can also tell us *when* something happened. They have different forms to show whether the action takes place in the present or in the past. The different forms of a verb are called **tenses**. The word *tense* refers to *time.*

If a verb is in the **present tense**, the action is taking place now. If a verb is in the **past tense**, the action took place at some previous time.

Verbs that form the past tense by adding *-d* or *-ed* are called **regular verbs.** Forming the past tense of most regular verbs is not difficult if you remember these rules.

1   If the present tense ends in *e,* add *-d.* (*save — saved*)

2   If the present tense does not end in *e,* add *-ed.* (*miss — missed*)

3   If the present tense ends in a *y* preceded by a consonant, change the *y* to *i* and add *-ed.* (*carry — carried*)

4   If the present tense ends in a single consonant preceded by a short vowel, double the consonant before adding *-ed.* (*stop — stopped*)

J.   Write the past tense form of these regular verbs. After each one, write the number of the rule you used to give the correct answer.

1. embarrass _____   8. cancel _____

2. wrap _____   9. hurry _____

3. transfer _____   10. collapse _____

4. study _____   11. snore _____

5. disagree _____   12. attack _____

6. plan _____   13. deny _____

7. worry _____   14. drag _____

Unit 7

Choosing the Right Meaning

Many words in English have more than one meaning. If you looked up the word *face* in your dictionary, you would probably find an entry like the one at the right. Ten different meanings of the word are listed. Each definition is followed by a phrase or sentence in italics showing how that meaning of the word would be used. In most dictionaries, the more common definitions of the word are listed first.

> **face** (fās) **1** the front part of the head: *The eyes, nose, and mouth are parts of the face.* **2** a look or expression: *His face was sad.* **3** an ugly or peculiar look made by twisting or distorting one's face: *The boy made a face at his sister.* **4** the front part; the surface: *the face of the earth.* **5** the side of a watch, clock, card, etc. that shows the numbers or signs: *He turned one of the cards face upwards.* **6** in geometry, one of the flat surfaces of a solid: *A cube has six faces.* **7** outward appearance: *This action, on the face of it, looks bad.* **8** to front toward: *The house faces the street. The picture faces page 60 in my book.* **9** meet; confront; stand up to: *He had the courage to face his problems.* **10** turn in the direction of; take a position opposite to: *He was told to face the wall. One dancer faced the other.* **11** cover with something, especially a different material: *That wooden house is being faced with brick.* 1-7 *n.*, 8-11 *v.*, **faced, fac·ing**
>
> *Copyright © 1985, Gage Junior Dictionary*

A. Use your dictionary to look up the word in italics in each of the following sentences. Read all the definitions carefully. On the line below each sentence, write the meaning that "makes sense" in that particular sentence.

1. The boys drew *lots* to decide who would go first.

_____

2. The soldiers had just come back from the *front*.

_____

3. The *cast* is listed on page 3 of the program.

_____

4. How do you *temper* steel?

_____

5. Let's *pool* our money and buy a pizza.

_____

6. The *square* of seven is forty-nine.

_____

7. Stop *needling* your brother!

_____

8. Karen plans to photograph the eagles from a *blind*.

_____

B. The dictionary can also be used to find information quickly. Find the answers to these questions by looking up the italicized words. Answer in complete sentences.

1. If you visited the *marsupial* section of the zoo, what animals might you see?

_____

2. Which animal has *flukes*?

_____

3. What would a group of *numismatists* probably discuss at a meeting?

_____

4. Which sport would you watch in a *velodrome*?

_____

5. On which animal would you ride in a *howdah*?

_____

6. Why might your father visit a *haberdasher*?

_____

7. Where in your body is the *malleus* located?

_____

8. Where would you probably be if you saw *picadors*?

_____

9. What could you use a *calabash* for?

_____

10. What part of your body would hurt if you had *pyorrhea*?

_____

11. What would you find in an *arboretum*?

_____

_____

_____

12. How many legs does a *decapod* have?

_____

_____

_____

"COOKED" LOBSTER

The Comma with Interrupters

To help explain our ideas, we sometimes use words or phrases that do not affect the meaning of the sentence. These expressions are called **interrupters**. They may come at the beginning, middle, or end of a sentence. Notice how interrupting words and expressions are set off with commas.

> *By the way*, I forgot to ask you to bring your accordion.
>
> You know, *of course*, that Shabana won't be here until noon.
>
> Katrina should arrive before ten o'clock, *however*.

C. Write sentences of your own using the following phrases as interrupters. Place the interrupter at the beginning of two of your sentences. In two sentences, position the interrupter in the middle. Place the interrupter at the end of two of your sentences. Check your work by reading the sentences *without* the interrupters. The meaning of the sentences should not change. Use commas wherever necessary.

1. on the other hand

_____

_____

2. after all

_____

_____

3. as a matter of fact

_____

_____

4. therefore

_____

_____

5. for instance

_____

_____

6. for example

_____

_____

Adding the Details

Before you start to write, you often have to collect detailed information. Remember that reference books are not the only places to get ideas. Sometimes you can talk to people who know a great deal about your topic.

The following paragraph discusses some of the strange places where bats roost. Notice how the author presents a series of details to illustrate the main idea in the topic sentence.

While most bats roost in caves, hollow trees, or attics, some live in unusual places. In Malaysia, club-footed bats squeeze inside the hollow joints of bamboo stalks through small holes made by boring beetles. Suction pads on their feet and wrists help them cling to the bamboo's smooth interior. Woolly bats in Africa often move into the basketlike nests of weaverbirds and sunbirds. In South America, tent-making bats use leaves from palm trees to make a tent which protects them from sun and rain. Because their skulls are flattened, South American flat-headed bats can squeeze into small openings and roost under rocks.

D. This paragraph talks about four of the unusual places in which bats live. List them.

1. _____

2. _____

3. _____

4. _____

E. Now it's your turn to write. The little brown bat lives everywhere in Canada except the far North. Here is some information about these bats. Do these details all belong in the same paragraph? Why?

1. Lose up to twenty-five percent of their weight during hibernation — fat stored in body almost gone by spring.
2. In early November, look for a cave in which to hibernate. Site must be warm enough to keep them from freezing.
3. In flight, utter a rapid series of high-pitched cries.
4. Emerge from caves in late April or May.
5. May change positions during the winter. Sometimes change caves.
6. Have few enemies — a few are caught by owls.
7. Don't eat all winter — may drink if awakened.
8. During winter, body temperature gradually drops from normal to match the environment.

Suppose you wanted to write a paragraph about how these bats hibernate. Cross out the two details you would not include. Arrange the remaining details in an order that makes sense. Then write the paragraph in your notebook. Be sure to begin with an interesting topic sentence that will arouse your reader's interest.

F. Choose one of the topic sentences you wrote for Exercise **A** in Unit 6. List at least six details you could use to explain more about the topic sentence. Arrange your details in a logical order. Then, write the paragraph in your notebook.

Irregular Verbs: Part 1

For most regular verbs, you form the past tense by adding -*d* or -*ed* to the present tense form. Some verbs, however, do not follow this pattern. They are called **irregular verbs**. Once, many of the verbs in English were irregular; now, there are only about one hundred left.

Let's look at some examples of irregular verbs. The **past participle** form is used after the helping verbs *has, have,* or *had.*

Present Tense (Today I)	Past Tense (Yesterday I)	Past Participle (Since last week I)
bring	brought	(have) brought
come	came	(have) come
do	did	(have) done
eat	ate	(have) eaten
give	gave	(have) given
go	went	(have) gone
see	saw	(have) seen
take	took	(have) taken

G. Complete each sentence with the past tense of the verb in parentheses. Remember to use the past participle after all helping verbs. Do not use the present tense.

1. One of the girls had _____ (bring) a magnifying glass.

2. Have you _____ (see) my car keys?

3. Patrick has already _____ (eat) his lunch.

4. Has Deborah _____ (take) a first aid course?

5. My father _____ (come) home early last night.

6. Nobody knew where Lydia had _____ (go).

7. Has Karl _____ (give) you the tickets?

8. We _____ (do) most of the work yesterday.

H. Write sentences in your notebook using each of these verb forms.

has done   have brought   has given   went   did

Unit 8

Irregular Verbs: Part 2

Read each of these verb forms aloud a number of times. Notice how the vowel changes from *i* to *a* to *u*.

Present Tense (Today I)	Past Tense (Yesterday I)	Past Participle (Since last week I)
begin	began	(have) begun
drink	drank	(have) drunk
ring	rang	(have) rung
sing	sang	(have) sung
sink	sank (or sunk)	(have) sunk
swim	swam	(have) swum

A. Complete each sentence with the past tense of the verb in parentheses. Remember to use the past participle after a helping verb. Do not use the present tense.

1. Has anyone _____ (swim) across the lake this year?

2. How much have they _____ (drink) today?

3. Yesterday, the snow _____ (begin) to fall about noon.

4. That bell has not _____ (ring) for thirty years.

5. Last Christmas, our choir _____ (sing) at Children's Hospital.

6. Has the water level _____ (sink) below five metres?

Checking for Sentences that Do Not Belong

When you edit, always check that detail sentences tell about the main idea in the topic sentence. Remove those sentences that don't belong.

B. Here are two paragraph about frogs. The topic sentences are printed in italics. Read each of the detail sentences carefully. Cross out the sentence in each paragraph that does not belong.

Here is how frogs get their food. Sitting motionless, they wait patiently for dinner to arrive. When an insect finally comes within range, the frog darts its long, sticky tongue forward with incredible speed and catches its victim on the forked tip. Instantly the insect is flicked back into the frog's mouth, tasted, and swallowed whole. Snakes swallow their food whole, too. These actions happen so fast that they can be seen only with slow motion photography.

Frogs have terrible eating habits. They do not chew their food politely. Instead, they swallow it whole in one great gulp. Larger prey is stuffed into their mouths with both hands, while tiny teeth on the upper jaw stop the meal from escaping. Adult frogs eat mainly insects and other small animals such as earthworms and spiders. Incredibly, to help get its food down, the frog even pulls its eyes way back into their sockets and uses them to help shove the food down its throat. Its eyes actually drop into its head and pop out again!

1. Which of the two topic sentences do you think is the more effective? Why did you choose this sentence?

_____

_____

2. Now rewrite the topic sentence you feel should be improved so it will catch the reader's attention.

_____

_____

Making Subjects and Verbs Agree

In English, verbs and their subjects must always **agree** or match. If the subject is singular, the verb must be singular. If the subject is plural, the verb must be plural.

My sister *plays* baseball every Saturday.

My sisters *play* baseball every Saturday.

In the first sentence, the singular verb *plays* is used to agree with the singular noun *sister*. In the second sentence, the plural verb *play* agrees with the plural noun *sisters*. Notice that, unlike nouns, the singular form of the verb ends with an *s* when some third person (other than I or you) is the subject.

You know that every sentence must have a subject and a predicate. Within the complete subject is a key word called the **simple subject** that tells exactly *who* or *what* the sentence is about. The simple subject is usually a noun.

When there's only one noun in the complete subject, finding the simple subject is easy.

Muddy *water* covered the floor of the cabin.

When the complete subject contains two or more nouns, however, choosing the simple subject is more difficult. Let's look at an example.

The five *boys* on the *bench* cheered loudly.

In this sentence you must decide which of the two nouns in italics is the simple subject. To do this, ask yourself, "Who or what does the action in this sentence?" Obviously, it was the boys and not the bench that "cheered loudly." The noun *boys*, therefore, is the simple subject.

C. In each of the following sentences, draw one line under the complete subject and circle the noun that is the simple subject. Remember, the subject is not always at the beginning of the sentence!

Example:

The covered (bridge) near my uncle's farm is almost one hundred years old.

1. The apples in that box are rotten.

2. The keys for my father's car slid off the dock.

3. The windows on this side of the cabin need cleaning.

4. Slowly the two horses pulled the heavy hay wagon up the hill.

5. The dishes on the table once belonged to the king of France.

6. During the storm, the maple tree near the garage blew down.

7. Tomorrow the students in our class are going on a field trip.

8. Through his binoculars, the man on the horse watched the mountain sheep.

9. Early this morning the girl in the blue pants caught seven fish.

10. The lights in the palace windows went out at ten o'clock.

Don't be fooled when a group of words called a phrase comes between the subject and the verb.

The water *in those lakes* is polluted.

In this sentence the phrase *in those lakes* comes between the simple subject and the verb. Notice, however, that the verb *is* agrees with the simple subject *water*, not the noun in the phrase.

D. Circle the simple subject in each of the following sentences. If the simple subject is singular, write "S" under it. If it is plural, write "P." Draw an arrow from the subject to the verb it agrees with.

Example:

The (bicycle) with the red fenders (belong, belongs) to my sister.

1. The students in our school (is, are) going to the hockey game tonight.

2. The owner of the dogs (was, were) phoned by the police.

3. The magazine under your notebooks (is, are) overdue.

4. A box of peaches (costs, cost) twelve dollars.

5. The list of rules (is, are) five pages long.

6. The people in the principal's office (is, are) police officers.

7. The tires on that car (need, needs) replacing immediately.

8. The players on that team (wears, wear) blue and yellow uniforms.

9. The books on that shelf (is, are) about Alberta.

10. The girls on the bridge (was, were) shouting at the man in the kayak.

Making Verbs Agree with Compound Subjects

Making the verb agree with the subject is usually not difficult. Sometimes you may have problems, however, when the subject is **compound**, or made up of more than one part. Study the following rules and examples.

1 Parts joined by *and*:

When the parts of a compound subject are joined by *and*, the verb is always plural, even if the parts themselves are singular.

Lyle and Jamie **are** going fishing.   *Leopards and jaguars* **live** in tropical countries.

2 Parts joined by *or, nor, either-or,* or *neither-nor*:

a. If both of the parts are singular, use a singular verb.

Neither the hat nor the jacket **fits** properly.

b. If both of the parts are plural, use a plural verb.

Either buses or trucks **travel** in that lane.

c. If one part is singular and one part is plural, the verb agrees with the part nearer to it.

Neither my uncle nor my cousins **are** coming.   *Neither my cousins nor my uncle* **is** coming.

E. Underline the complete subjects in each of the following sentences. Write the correct form of the verb in parentheses in the blank at the right.

1. Tim and Bruce (has, have) visited Austria.

2. Neither hawks nor owls (eats, eat) seeds.

3. The cat and the dog (is, are) sleeping.

4. Either Mr. Smith or the janitor (has, have) the keys to that room.

5. Old books and torn paper (cover, covers) the floor.

6. Daffodils and tulips (grow, grows) along the sidewalk.

7. Either the principal or Ms.Mason (is, are) wrong.

8. Neither the milk nor the meat (smells, smell) fresh.

9. Louise or her mother always (makes, make) supper at six o'clock.

10. The sweater and the blouse (matches, match) the skirt.

1. _____

2. _____

3. _____

4. _____

5. _____

6. _____

7. _____

8. _____

9. _____

10. _____

Exact Verbs Bring the Action to Life

When you edit, always look carefully at your verbs. Try to use exact verbs that will help your reader see, hear, smell, or taste the action you are describing.

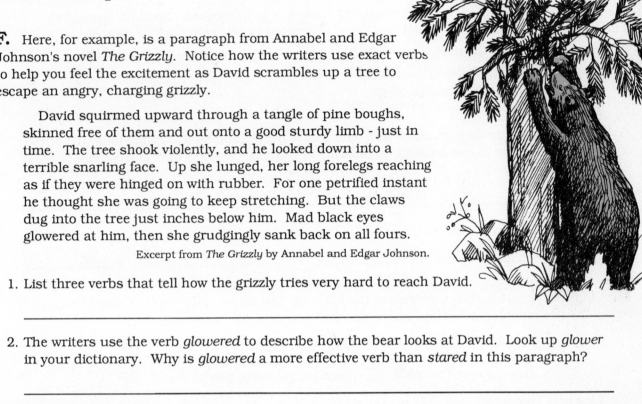

F. Here, for example, is a paragraph from Annabel and Edgar Johnson's novel *The Grizzly*. Notice how the writers use exact verbs to help you feel the excitement as David scrambles up a tree to escape an angry, charging grizzly.

> David squirmed upward through a tangle of pine boughs, skinned free of them and out onto a good sturdy limb - just in time. The tree shook violently, and he looked down into a terrible snarling face. Up she lunged, her long forelegs reaching as if they were hinged on with rubber. For one petrified instant he thought she was going to keep stretching. But the claws dug into the tree just inches below him. Mad black eyes glowered at him, then she grudgingly sank back on all fours.
>
> Excerpt from *The Grizzly* by Annabel and Edgar Johnson.

1. List three verbs that tell how the grizzly tries very hard to reach David.

_____

2. The writers use the verb *glowered* to describe how the bear looks at David. Look up *glower* in your dictionary. Why is *glowered* a more effective verb than *stared* in this paragraph?

_____

3. Find the verb *looked* in the thesaurus at the back of this book. In your notebook list at least five other words that mean "looked." Write interesting sentences showing the exact meaning of each of the verbs you select.

G. Write three exact verbs for each of these general verbs.

1. eat   _____   5. fall   _____

2. walk   _____   6. put   _____

3. break   _____   7. call   _____

4. pull   _____   8. look   _____

H. All the verbs below mean "to move in a particular way." In your notebook, write an interesting sentence using each of these verbs. Check the meaning of those you are unsure of in your dictionary. You may use more than one verb in a sentence.

trudged shuffled ambled pranced skimmed scudded
skittered sauntered hurtled loped flitted lurched

Unit 9

The Comma in Direct Address

In each of the following sentences, someone is spoken to or **addressed**. Read the sentences quietly to yourself. Listen for a slight pause in your voice as you read each sentence.

Alan, please close the door.

Your daughter, Mrs.Jones, just won a thousand dollars.

Did you finish your homework, girls?

A. Circle the noun in each sentence that tells who is being addressed. On the following lines, write a rule about the use of commas with nouns in address. When is only one comma needed? When are two required?

_____

_____

_____

B. Circle the nouns in direct address in the following sentences. Add commas where necessary. Remember, commas are also used with place names and words in a series.

1. Dad do you know the population of Brandon Manitoba?

2. Sarah just called Jessica to ask if you wanted to go skiing this weekend.

3. Your first answer Michael was correct.

4. Mrs.Anderson wants to see you Fiona.

5. Remember boys to bring your running shoes bathing suits and cameras.

When Subjects Follow the Verb

In many sentences, the subject comes before the verb. If a sentence begins with the introductory words *here* or *there*, however, the subject usually follows the verb. When you start a sentence with one of these words, ask yourself, "Will the subject be singular or plural?" Use the verb form that agrees with the subject.

Here is the book you wanted.

There are four keys missing from the drawer.

In informal conversation, people often use the contraction *there's* even though the subject is plural. To be correct, they should say,

There are ten horses in the next race.

The subject often follows the verb in questions, too.

When were the boys coming?

Has the bus from Pincher Creek arrived yet?

C. In each of the following sentences, underline the noun that is the simple subject. Above the noun, write "S" if the subject is singular or "P" if it is plural. Write the form of the verb that agrees with the subject in the blank at the right.

1. (There's, There are) three horses in the barn.

1. _____

2. There (go, goes) the fire alarm.

2. _____

3. (Was, Were) there any cookies in the tin?

3. _____

4. There (is, are) six strings on a guitar.

4. _____

5. (Is, Are) there any pencils in that drawer?

5. _____

6. (Has, Have) the cat been fed yet?

6. _____

7. (Was, Were) the drapes cleaned last month?

7. _____

8. There (is, are) only one car on the ferry.

8. _____

9. (Was, Were) the twins coming?

9. _____

10. Here (is, are) the book you wanted.

10. _____

Getting to Know the Greeks and Latins

The space age began on October 4, 1957, when a rocket roared into space carrying Sputnik I, the first artificial satellite to circle the earth. Twelve years later, American astronaut Neil Armstrong walked on the moon. On October 8, 1984, Marc Garneau became the first Canadian to travel and work in space.

Although space exploration is quite recent, many of the words used in space research are very old. In Canada and the United States, space explorers are called *astronauts*. This word comes from two ancient Greek words meaning "sailor among the stars." In the Soviet Union, space travellers are "sailors in the universe" or *cosmonauts*. The section of the spacecraft that carries the astronauts is known as a *capsule* from the Latin *capsula* meaning "little box." Satellites use *telemetry* to send information about conditions in outer space back to earth. *Telemetry* is from the Greek words *tele* and *meter* meaning "to measure at a distance."

English has borrowed words from all the major languages of the world. Over half our words, however, come from Greek and Latin, the language spoken by the ancient Romans. Because so many English words come from these languages, learning a few key Greek and Latin root words can help you understand the meaning of thousands of English words. Just as a tree root is the base from which a tree develops, so a **root word** is a word from which other words grow. The chart on page 44 contains some of the most common Greek and Latin roots.

Root	Meaning	Example	Root	Meaning	Example
annus	year	annual	dynamis	power	dynamite
aqua	water	aquarium	geo	earth	geologist
astro	star	astronaut	graph	write	biography
aud	hear	audience	mare	sea	Maritimes
auto	self	autograph	meter	measure	thermometer
bio	life	biology	ped	foot	pedestrian
centum	hundred	century	script	write	scribble
cycl	circle	bicycle	tele	distant	telegraph
dent	tooth	dental	thermo	heat	thermostat

D. The following word search contains the twenty-nine following words with Greek and Latin roots.

annual tricycle thermos televise pedestrian telescope perennial
telephoto scribe pedicure astrology dental cyclone pedal audible
dentist cyclist marina barometer denture biologist aquatic marine
centurion geology dynamo geography dynamic biology

```
G X P P C A E X S O M A N Y D C
E H S E I N R E L C Y C I R T Y
L N A R M N U N O I R U T N E C
B A S E A U C D E N T I S T D L
I I T N N A I P L E Z Q B W P I
D R R N Y L D X L B J Q J E H S
U T O I D H E A L A T N E D T
A S L A D E P R N C I T A U Q A
D E O L Q H O A I Y Y T D N N Y
E D G S O M C V R K G C V Z Y P
N E Y T E M S F A G E O L O G Y
T P O T W D E W M V O Q L O R D
U F E J T E L E V I S E V O N M
R R C D T H E R M O S R G M I E
E N I R A M T T S I G O L O I B
```

Find the hidden words by reading down, across, or diagonally. Some are written forward, others backward. Words may overlap so that some letters are used for more than one word. Circle each word when you find it and look it up in a dictionary. Then write interesting sentences in your notebook showing clearly what each word means.

Irregular Verbs: Part 3

Present Tense (Today I)	Past Tense (Yesterday I)	Past Participle (Since last week I)
break	broke	(have) broken
choose	chose	(have) chosen
freeze	froze	(have) frozen
speak	spoke	(have) spoken
tear	tore	(have) torn
wear	wore	(have) worn
blow	blew	(have) blown
grow	grew	(have) grown
know	knew	(have) known
throw	threw	(have) thrown

E. Complete each sentence with the past tense of the verb in parentheses. Remember to use the past participle after all helping verbs. Do not use the present tense.

1. Last year my uncle _____ (grow) tomatoes in that greenhouse.

2. Have you _____ (speak) to Mrs. Singh today?

3. The boat's mast _____ (break) during the hurricane.

4. I have _____ (know) Janice for five years.

5. Those pipes have been _____ (freeze) since Tuesday.

6. Have the coaches _____ (choose) the members of the all-star team?

7. Why didn't you mention that you had _____ (tear) your jacket?

8. We must have _____ (blow) up at least sixty balloons for the party.

9. You should have _____ (throw) the ball to the pitcher.

10. Couldn't Jim have _____ (wear) his brother's uniform?

Practising Editing Skills

Imagine you work for a newspaper. A reporter has just sent in a story about an earthquake along the Adriatic coast of Yugoslavia, a country in southeastern Europe. This area has numerous resorts and small fishing villages. Directly behind many of the settlements are high cliffs. The harbors are always full of pleasure boats, fishing vessels, and ocean-going liners.

F. You've been asked to edit the reporter's story. As you read the following paragraph, think about how it could be improved.

On Easter Sunday the coast of Yugoslavia had a bad earthquake. In the towns, streets cracked. Some cars went into these cracks. Some trucks and buses went in, too. Big stones fell from the surrounding cliffs. They hit store windows. They hit the walls of shops, houses, and hotels, too. A castle, more than five hundred years old, went into the sea. The earthquake caused a big wave. It hit the shore. Many things along the shore were destroyed. Fortunately, it was Sunday morning. Many people were outside. Some were on their way to church. Others were going to the market. Luckily, only ninety-four people died.

1. If you were to edit this paragraph, what changes would you make? Try to think of at least three ways to improve the report.

_____

_____

_____

2. The writer of this paragraph used too many short sentences. Mark the sentences you think could be combined.

3. Now, edit the paragraph in your notebook making these changes:

   a. Rewrite the topic sentence to catch the reader's attention.

   b. Join sentences wherever you can.

   c. Use a thesaurus to find substitutes for overworked words such as *bad* and *big*. Replace vague verbs, such as *went*, *hit*, and *fell*, with more exact words.

   d. In this paragraph the writer says, "Many things along the shore were destroyed." What do you think might have been destroyed? As you rewrite, replace the vague phrase *many things* with some specific examples of your own.

Unit 10

Arranging Details in Logical Order

Giving directions involves explaining how to get somewhere or how to make or do something. A good set of directions is clear, complete, well organized, and easy to follow. Suppose you decided to repaint your bedroom. If you had to follow this set of directions, what problems would you have?

1. Start painting the ceiling in a corner and work across the width of the wall.
2. Take as much of the furniture out of the room as possible.
3. Paint the ceiling first, then the walls, and finally the woodwork.
4. Remove doorknobs, curtain rods, and plates over switches and outlets.
5. To keep the remaining furniture clean, cover with plastic sheets.
6. Clean brushes and rollers well and hang to dry.
7. Thoroughly wash painted walls and all woodwork.
8. Patch cracks with a filler and sand smooth.
9. Start at the top of the walls and paint in narrow strips to the bottom.

When you're giving directions or explaining how to do something, always arrange the instructions in sequential order. Details arranged in the order in which they should be followed are said to be in **time** or **chronological order.**

A. Study the directions for painting a room. On the following line, write the numbers of the steps in chronological order.

_____

B. Once you have the directions in the right order, write a paragraph in your notebook explaining how to paint a bedroom. But don't simply recopy the directions. Help your reader move easily from one step to the next by adding ordering words and phrases such as *before you start, then, next,* and *finally.* You will have to add words to some of the directions to make them into complete sentences. Remember to start your paragraph with an interesting topic sentence.

C. Read the following set of directions. Then rewrite the directions, making them more specific, on the lines under the paragraph and on page 48. Use your imagination to add details.

I think I can tell you how to find the post office. To get there go down this road for some distance until you come to a large building. Turn north and drive for five or ten minutes. After a while you should come to a lake. I think the post office is somewhere in the shopping centre at the far end of the lake.

_____

_____

_____

_____

_____

_____

_____

_____

D. Suppose you learned on May 15 that you have a job as a group leader at a summer camp for children eight and nine years old. The camp director has written a letter giving you some information about the job. In her letter she points out that each group leader must be prepared to demonstrate how to make something. The camp has some simple tools but not a lot of materials. She would like you to send her a clear, simple, and complete set of directions for your project so she can include them in a booklet to be given to the campers.

Decide what you would like to have the campers construct. Be sure to choose something that children of this age could build. Before you begin writing, take time to list the steps involved. Once your set of directions is complete and in order, write the paragraph in your notebook. Test your paragraph by asking a younger student to follow your directions.

Checking Up on Sentence Variety

E. In each of the following sentences the subject is at the beginning. Rewrite the sentences, placing the subjects at the end.

Example:

The large spider dangled just above my head.

Just above my head dangled the large spider.

1. A terrifying shriek came from deep inside the gloomy cave.

_____

2. Three large black and orange bugs crawled out of the drain in the bathtub.

_____

3. The band from Redfern School marched smartly onto the field.

_____

4. An unusual burping sound came from under the seat of the abandoned car.

_____

5. A massive black cloud suddenly appeared over Mount Robson.

_____

F. Underline the subject in each of these sentences. Then, rewrite each sentence putting the subject in a different place.

Example:

The <u>magician</u> sawed my mother in half at the end of his performance.

At the end of his performance, the magician sawed my mother in half.

1. The detective found the stolen diamonds in an old pickle jar in the hayloft.

   _____

2. Hidden under a blanket in a large trunk in my grandfather's attic, I found seven baby porcupines.

   _____

3. On the far side of the meadow lived a lively colony of prairie dogs.

   _____

4. Roald Amundsen, a Norwegian explorer, reached the South Pole on December 14, 1911.

   _____

5. Near the small raft on which the girls crouched appeared an enormous black fin.

   _____

Checking Up on Subject-Verb Agreement

G. Circle the simple subject in each of the following sentences. Then write the verb that agrees with the subject in the blank at the right.

Example:

A (box) of apples (cost, costs) seven dollars.   *costs*

1. The books on the table (is, are) my sister's.   1. _____

2. There (was, were) twenty-five people at the party.   2. _____

3. Every ticket for the play (has, have) been sold.   3. _____

4. Beside the garage (is, are) two apple trees.   4. _____

5. (Is, Are) there any seats left in the balcony?   5. _____

6. (Has, Have) the movie started?   6. _____

7. There (is, are) several ways to reach the top.   7. _____

8. (Was, Were) Bill or Jennifer coming?   8. _____

9. Where (is, are) your sister's binoculars?   9. _____

10. There (is, are) three cars in the driveway.   10. _____

Changing Meanings with Prefixes

A **prefix** is a word part that comes before the base, or root word, to change its meaning. Let's look at some examples.

If a napkin is not *folded*, then it is *un*folded.

If you and your friend do not *agree*, then you *dis*agree.

If the furniture in your room is *arranged* in a different way, then it is *re*arranged.

The word *prefix* is made up of the Latin word *figere*, meaning "to fasten," and the prefix *pre-*, meaning "before."

Knowing the meanings of common prefixes will often help you with the meaning of a new word. For example, if you know the prefix *semi-* means "half" or "partly," you would have no problem understanding *semicircle* (half a circle) or *semiconscious* (partly conscious). The following chart shows you five common prefixes, their meanings, and some examples.

Prefix	Meaning	Examples
pre-	before	preschool, prearrange
re-	again, once more	reread, repay, rewrite
sub-	under, below	subtopic, submarine
super-	above, beyond, over	superhuman, supertanker
trans-	across, over	transatlantic, transplant

H. Complete each of the sentences, below, with one of the following words. Use each word only once.

prefabricated semiweekly subsonic reorganize supernatural transported predicts subcommittee supercharger semifinal prehistoric subtopics transfusion recount rescheduled

Example:

Much of the wheat from the prairies is

transported

to Vancouver by train.

1. _____ planes fly slower than the speed of sound.

2. Scientists learn much about _____ life by studying fossils.

3. A magazine published twice a week is a _____ .

4. A miracle is a _____ event.

5. As the injured police officer had lost so much blood, the doctor decided to give her a

_____ .

6. Large sections of _____ buildings are made in

factories and then shipped to the building site.

7. The winners of the two _____ games will play for

the championship on Saturday afternoon.

8. A device for forcing more than the usual amount of air and gasoline into a car's cylinders is

called a _____ .

9. Because so many players had been injured, the football coach had to

_____ the team.

10. Four people from the large committee formed a _____

to solve the problem.

11. He divided his report on computers into five _____ .

12. The weather forecaster _____ a blizzard tomorrow.

13. Because it rained all night, the game will be _____ .

14. Ted asked for a _____ because he lost the

election by only one vote.

I. Find three words in the dictionary that begin with each of these prefixes: *sub, super, semi,* and *pre.* Don't choose words from the list in Exercise H. Try to select words that are new to you. Then, in your notebook, write an interesting sentence using each of your words.

Checking Up on Punctuation

J. Draw three lines under all letters that should be capitalized. Insert commas where necessary.

1. our next game paul is on saturday november 7 at regent park.

2. in football the clock stops after each incomplete pass after a team scores and when a player

   is injured.

3. did you know that the roughriders lost only two games last year gail?

4. an earthquake in tangshan china on july 28 1976 killed 148 000 people.

5. the echidna also called a spiny anteater uses its strong claws long beak and sticky tongue to

   rip ant nests apart.

it 11

Using Prefixes to Make Antonyms

A prefix added to a word often forms the **antonym**, or opposite, of the base word. Three common prefixes that act in this way are *un-* (unlucky), *in-* (invisible), and *dis-* (dislike). Before words beginning with the letters *m* or *p*, the prefix *in-* changes to *im-* (impolite).

A. Write the antonym of each of the words listed below by adding the prefix *un-*, *in-* (*im-*), or *dis-*. Use your dictionary if you are not sure which prefix is correct.

Example:

healthy *unhealthy*

1. willing _____

2. frequent _____

3. movable _____

4. prove _____

5. organized _____

6. believable _____

7. mature _____

8. known _____

9. like _____

10. capable _____

11. connect _____

12. polite _____

13. friendly _____

14. curable _____

15. welcome _____

16. experienced _____

17. trust _____

18. complete _____

19. satisfactory _____

20. probable _____

Developing Paragraphs with Examples

A paragraph can be put together or **developed** in many ways. When you're deciding how to organize your thoughts, always go back to the main idea of the paragraph. Then ask yourself two questions:

What point am I trying to get across in this paragraph?

What's the best way to make this main idea clear to the reader?

Often the best way to make your paragraph easier to understand is to arrange the details in time or chronological order. You can also make your writing clear with a series of examples.

B. Read the following paragraph carefully. The main idea is clearly stated in the topic sentence, *Your classroom is quite different from those in ancient China.* In the sentences that follow, the writer gives specific examples of *how* early Chinese classrooms were different from yours.

Your classroom is quite different from those in ancient China. Girls did not attend early Chinese schools. Only the sons of wealthier people went to school, as poorer parents needed their sons to help at home. Because printing had not been invented, pupils did not use books. Instead, the teacher simply recited a phrase and the students repeated it aloud. The school day lasted from dawn to dusk. Discipline was strict, and boys who did not work were severely beaten. If students were careless in their writing, they were made to drink a dish of ink.

C. Now it's your turn to write and use your imagination. What do you think classrooms will be like in the year 2025? How might computers and videodisks be used? What role will robots play in twenty-first century classrooms? What subjects will be important in the school of the future? How might the teacher's job be different from today?

Begin by listing some examples that show the possible differences between the twenty-first century classroom and yours. Be specific. Do not, for example, simply list *computers*, but explain how computers might actually be used in future classrooms.

1. _____
2. _____
3. _____
4. _____
5. _____
6. _____
7. _____

Now write a paragraph using the examples in your plan. Be sure to start with an interesting topic sentence.

Exploring with Interviews

A conversation in which you collect information from someone about a topic is called an **interview**. In interviews, people ask questions and record the answers. The word *interview* comes from a French word meaning "to visit with each other."

Good interviewers often research a topic in preparation for an interview. Before interviewing someone, take time to jot down what you'd like to know. Then, using your notes, make up questions that are clear and easy to understand. By preparing carefully, you'll be able to talk intelligently during the interview. If you want to collect useful information to write about, don't ask questions that can be answered with "yes" or "no." These answers won't tell you enough. Be sure to ask follow-up questions if you need more details.

D. Interview an older person in your community to find out what classrooms were like when he or she went to school. Before you start, list six questions you could ask. Remember to avoid questions that call for "yes" or "no" answers.

1. _____

2. _____

3. _____

4. _____

5. _____

6. _____

Once you have collected the information, write the paragraph in your notebook.

Combining Ideas with Compounds

Short sentences can often be combined by using a **compound subject**. Let's look at an example:

> Last summer, my sister visited Dawson City. Her friend Tanya went with her.

Now let's rewrite the sentences using a compound subject.

> Last summer, my sister and her friend Tanya visited Dawson City.

Sentences with the same subjects can often be combined by using a **compound predicate**, as in the following example.

The stallion pawed the ground. Then he snorted angrily.

The stallion pawed the ground and snorted angrily.

E. Combine each of the following groups of sentences by using a compound subject or a compound predicate. Leave out any unnecessary words.

1. The fire fighters crawled into the smoke-filled plane. They tried desperately to rescue the unconscious passengers.

   _____

   _____

2. Cow Head is a small town on the west coast of Newfoundland. Another small town in the same area is Parson's Pond.

   _____

   _____

3. Rick decorated the gymnasium for the Halloween party. Three of his friends helped him.

   _____

   _____

4. Anacondas wrap their coils around an enemy in a fight. Pythons fight in the same way.

   _____

   _____

5. The mother sea turtle dug a hole in the sand. Next she laid her eggs. Then she covered them with sand. Once the eggs were covered, she returned to the sea.

   _____

   _____

6. The camel can go several days or even weeks without water. Many desert snakes can survive without water for a long time, too.

   _____

   _____

Pronouns: Substitutes for Nouns

Have you ever had a substitute teacher? A substitute is someone who replaces your regular teacher. In language, words that replace or substitute for nouns are called **pronouns**. The prefix *pro-* means "for" or "in place of." A pronoun is a word used in place of a noun.

Good writers use pronouns so they don't constantly repeat the same noun. Which of these sentences sounds better to you?

Mrs. Brown asked Bob to take off *Bob's* shoes so *Bob* wouldn't mark *Mrs. Brown's* carpets.

Mrs. Brown asked Bob to take off *his* shoes so *he* wouldn't mark *her* carpets.

In the second sentence, *his*, *he*, and *her* are pronouns used in place of the nouns *Bob* and *Mrs.Brown*. Notice how the pronouns make the sentence shorter and easier to read and understand.

F. Rewrite the following sentences in your notebook. Replace the nouns in italics with pronouns.

1. Tom took *Tom's* watch to Mr.Stevens so *Mr.Stevens* could repair *Tom's watch*.

2. The old man told Ellen and Judy to leave the cat alone as *the cat* might scratch *Ellen and Judy* if *Ellen and Judy* bothered *the cat*.

3. While visiting in Germany, Fred and *Fred's* sister bought a cuckoo clock which *Fred and Fred's sister* shipped to *Fred and Fred's sister's* mother in London.

4. Celia didn't just close the door. *Celia* slammed *the door*.

5. Ed studied the map carefully before putting *the map* back in *Ed's* pack.

G. The pronouns in the following sentences are printed in italics. Write one of the pronouns in each blank. Beside each pronoun write the noun it stands for.

Example:

"Jill and *I* will be late," replied Chet.

I - Chet

1. Sharon doesn't have the keys. *She* left *them* at home.

2. "But Dad promised *he* would take Scott and *me* to the hockey game," said Carolyn.

3. "Do *you* want to go with *us*, Randy?" asked Beth and Marie.

4. "Sam and *I* won two thousand dollars at bingo last night," replied Aunt Josie. "*We're* planning a trip to Mexico to celebrate."

5. "Mr.Wittenberg asked *us* to come," replied the boys. "*He* suggested *we* meet *him* here at seven o'clock."

6. When *they* came back from shopping, the twins hung *their* jackets in the hall.

7. Toronto is the largest city in Canada. *It's* also the capital of Ontario.

1. _____
2. _____
3. _____
4. _____
5. _____
6. _____
7. _____
8. _____
9. _____
10. _____
11. _____
12. _____
13. _____
14. _____
15. _____

Unit 12
Pronouns and Antecedents Must Agree

Like nouns, pronouns may be either singular or plural. Here is a list of common pronouns. Notice that *you, your,* and *yours* may be either singular or plural.

	Singular Pronouns	**Plural Pronouns**
Person speaking:	I, me, my, mine	we, us, our, ours
Person spoken to:	you, your, yours	you, your, yours
Another person, place, or thing it, its	he, him, his she, her, hers	they, them, their theirs

The noun that a pronoun stands for or replaces is called an **antecedent**. Let's look at an example.

"Mr. Nelson told us he would be here by nine o'clock," replied the girls.

In this sentence the antecedent of the pronoun *us* is the noun *girls.* The antecedent of the pronoun *he* is the noun *Mr. Nelson.*

A pronoun must always agree with its antecedent. If the antecedent is singular, the pronoun must be singular.

John tried, but he couldn't move the heavy box.

If the antecedent is plural, the pronoun must be plural.

The football players tried, but they couldn't move the heavy box.

Sometimes a pronoun's antecedent is another pronoun. When one of the following pronouns is the antecedent of a personal pronoun, the personal pronoun is always singular.

anybody   anyone   anything   each   either   neither   everybody

everyone   everything   nobody   no one   somebody   someone   one

Here are some examples:

Neither of my brothers has *his* driver's licence.

Someone on the girls' grass hockey team left *her* jacket on the bus.

Some pronouns are always plural. When one of the following pronouns is the antecedent of a personal pronoun, the personal pronoun must be plural.

both   few   many   several

Here are some examples:

Both of my sisters had the radios in *their* cars stolen.

Several of the dogs had porcupine quills in *their* noses.

A. In each of the following sentences, circle the simple subject. Beside each subject write "S" if the subject is singular or "P" is the subject is plural. Then, write the pronoun that correctly completes each sentence in the blank at the right. In some sentences, more than one pronoun may be correct.

Example:

S (Neither) of the girls brought (her, their) skis. _____her_____

1. One of the men had lost (his, their) wallet.

    1. _____

2. Several of the women took off (her, their) coats.

    2. _____

3. Nobody raised (her, his, their) hand.

    3. _____

4. Both of the trucks had (its, their) windshields broken.

    4. _____

5. One of my friends left (her, his, their) wet bathing suit on the sofa.

    5. _____

6. Only one of the girls has (her, their) lunch.

    6. _____

7. Neither of the dogs ate (its, their) supper.

    7. _____

8. Several of the cups have lost (its, their) handles.

    8. _____

9. Has anyone forgotten (his, her, their) tickets?

    9. _____

10. Both of the teams from Pineview School won (its, their) game.

    10. _____

11. Each of the players buys (her, his, their) own uniform.

    11. _____

12. Many of the turtles laid (its, their) eggs in the sand.

    12. _____

13. Someone is at the door, and (he, she, they) wants to speak to you.

    13. _____

14. Has anyone finished reading (her, his, their) novel?

    14. _____

15. Has each of the girls in the play learned (her, their) part?

    15. _____

16. Everyone did (his, her, their) best.

    16. _____

17. All of the boys have (his, their) raincoats.

    17. _____

18. If anyone needs a pen, (he, she, they) may borrow mine.

    18. _____

19. Many of the girls finished (her, their) projects yesterday.

    19. _____

20. Nobody left (her, his, their) seat.

    20. _____

Making Verbs Agree with Pronoun Subjects

When you use one of the pronouns you studied in the first part of this unit as the subject of the sentence, be sure the verb agrees with the subject. Let's look at some examples.

> *Neither* of the movies *is* very exciting.

In this sentence the singular verb *is* agrees with the singular subject *neither*.

> *Several* of my relatives *live* in Hong Kong.

Here, the plural verb *live* is used to agree with the plural subject *several*.

B. Circle the simple subject in each of the following sentences. Beside each subject write "S" if the subject is singular or "P" if the subject is plural. Then, write the verb form in parentheses that correctly completes each sentence in the blank at the right.

Example:

(Neither) of these books (has, have) any pictures.　　　*has* ___

1. A few of those stamps (is, are) quite valuable.　　1. _____

2. Everyone in the class (gets, get) a certificate.　　2. _____

3. Several of the boys (play, plays) football every Saturday.　　3. _____

4. Many of the refugees (speak, speaks) English.　　4. _____

5. One of our cats (has, have) kittens.　　5. _____

6. No one (has, have) the right answer.　　6. _____

7. Several of my ancestors (is, are) from India.　　7. _____

8. Neither of his friends (know, knows) how to swim.　　8. _____

9. Everything in that store (was, were) expensive.　　9. _____

10. Nobody (want, wants) to play softball.　　10. _____

11. Few of the boys (has, have) their bicycles.　　11. _____

12. Each of the four players (has, have) ten cards.　　12. _____

13. Both of her answers (was, were) incorrect.　　13. _____

14. One of the apples (was, were) rotten.　　14. _____

15. Either you or your brother (has, have) to go.　　15. _____

Checking Up on Punctuation

C. Proofread the following sentences to find words that need capitals. Draw three short lines under each letter that should be capitalized. Add commas where needed.

Example:

the members of the fort henry guard are canadian university and community college students. they perform throughout the summer at old fort henry in kingston, ontario, using snidenfield rifles, first issued to the british army in 1886.

1. in september 1812 david stuart of the pacific fur company built fort kamloops the first white settlement in southern british columbia.

2. halifax is the largest city in atlantic canada and the capital of nova scotia.

3. in 1896 gold was discovered on bonanza creek near dawson city in the yukon.

4. lake louise in banff national park was named for princess louise queen victoria's daughter.

5. one of canada's largest colonies of white pelicans lives on some rocky islands in lavallée lake in prince albert national park two hundred kilometres north of saskatoon saskatchewan.

6. at rocky point prince edward island a monument to the reverend georges belcourt stands between saint augustine's church and the farmers' bank.

7. memorial university in st john's newfoundland was built as a memorial to those soldiers who died in world war I.

8. carved on the front gates of lower fort garry in selkirk manitoba are the names of the men sent to put down the red river rebellion in 1870.

9. the university of new brunswick in fredericton is the second-oldest university in canada.

10. the montreal museum of fine arts has a 5000-year-old chinese vase an egyptian figure from 2500 b.c. and many displays of inuit and indian handicrafts.

Number Prefixes

One of the most difficult events in the Olympic Games is the decathlon in which athletes compete in ten events. On the first day, they take part in a 100 metre dash, long jump, shot-put, high jump, and 400 metre run. On the second day, they do the 110 metre hurdles, discus throw, pole vault, javelin throw, and 1500 metre run.

The word *decathlon* comes from the ancient Roman word *decem*, meaning "ten." The same root word appears in *December*, the tenth month of the ancient Roman calendar. If an army is *decimated* in battle, a large number of soldiers are killed. (Originally, this word meant "to kill every tenth person.") How long is a decimetre? What would be the answer if you decupled six?

Here are some of the most common number prefixes in English.

Prefix	Meaning	Example
uni-	one	unicorn, unicycle
bi-	two	bicycle, biplane
tri-	three	triangle, trio
quad-, quart-	four	quadruplet, quartet
octa-, octo-	eight	octagon, octopus
dec-	ten	decade, decimal
cent-	hundred	centigrade, century
mega-	large	megalopolis, megaphone
micro-	small	microscope, microfilm
multi-	many	multitude, multimillionaire
omni-	all	omnipotent, omnipresent

D. Use number prefixes to complete the following exercises. Use your dictionary and encyclopedia if necessary.

1. Organisms so small they cannot be seen with the naked eye are called

_____ .

2. List three examples of decapods.

_____

3. A group of four musicians is called a quartet. A group of eight musicians would be called an

_____ .

4. Animals that eat plants are herbivorous while those that eat other animals are carnivorous.

Animals that eat both plants and animals are _____ .

5. Why is the French flag called a tricolor?

_____ .

6. Four children born at the same time to one mother are called

_____ .

7. If a city celebrates its bicentennial in 1995, when was it founded? _____

8. Sixty is the quadruple of fifteen. One thousand is the _____ of ten.

9. Someone who speaks two languages is bilingual. What would you call a person who speaks

many languages? _____

10. A metropolis is the most important city in a region. A heavily populated area made up of several cities is sometimes called a _____.

Are You Persuasive?

Have you ever tried to change someone's mind? Perhaps you've tried to convince your teacher that you really *did* study for a test. Maybe you've tried to persuade your parents that your brother should wash the dishes.

In this exercise, you'll have a chance to use your persuasive powers. Suppose the manager of your local tourist office has hired you to write the opening paragraph for a travel booklet about your area. Your job is to convince tourists that your region would be an ideal place to visit.

When you write, start with a topic sentence that will give the reader a general idea of your area. Then give reasons and examples that will support this idea. Use colorful, interesting words that will make your reader understand exactly what you're talking about. Conclude with a sentence that will restate the impression you've created in the first line.

Let's look at an example.

Clearwater Valley is one of the few places left where nature still has the upper hand. Here the skies are blue, not grey with smog. The lakes are blue, too, clean and crystal clear. The sounds you hear are the sounds of nature. Here meadowlarks sing, loons call, and leaves rustle in the trees. The air is fresh and smells like pine trees and freshly mown grass. It's the kind of place where you can swim or fish or camp or golf without half the world breathing down your neck. Here you can visit historic sites and intriguing museums without standing in line. This summer, visit Clearwater Valley, a place where nature thrives.

E. Answer these questions in your notebook.

1. What overall impression of Clearwater Valley did the writer create in the opening sentence?

2. List five examples the writer used to convince you that Clearwater Valley is a "natural" place.

3. What is the purpose of the last sentence in this paragraph?

F. Now it's your turn to write. Start by deciding the overall impression you'd like to give tourists about your region. Write your choice in your notebook. Then list at least five special features you could use to support this overall impression. Now draft the paragraph in your notebook. Be sure to begin with an interesting topic sentence.

Once you've completed your first draft, edit your work to ensure your nouns and verbs are specific. Gain sentence variety by making sure that all your sentences do not begin with the subject.

Unit 13

Making the Reference Clear

The word *ambiguous* means "having more than one possible meaning." A pronoun is ambiguous if it can refer to more than one noun. Read the following sentence carefully. Which girl has the correct answer?

Kay told Alice that *her* answer was correct.

In this sentence the pronoun *her* could refer to either *Kay* or *Alice*. Here's one way to make the meaning of the sentence clear.

"Your answer is correct, Alice," replied Kay.

A. In each of the following sentences, the antecedent of the italicized pronoun is ambiguous. Rewrite the sentences to make the meaning clear.

1. Sandy asked Barry to repeat what *he* had said.

_____

2. Take the labels off the bottles and then wash *them*.

_____

3. My uncle told my brother that *his* friends would arrive Monday.

_____

4. Take the screens off the windows and clean *them* thoroughly.

_____

5. We took the plants out of the boxes and stacked *them* in the corner.

_____

6. Take the shells off the peanuts before you eat *them*.

_____

7. The old man blew his nose with a large red handkerchief and then stuffed *it* into his pocket.

_____

_____

8. Dolores took the strawberries out of the boxes and threw *them* into the garbage can.

_____

_____

Checking Up on Subject-Verb Agreement

B. Circle the simple subject in each of the following sentences. Beside each subject write "S" if the subject is singular or "P" if the subject is plural. Then, write the verb form in parentheses that correctly completes each sentence in the blank at the right.

1. At the bottom of the trunk (was, were) two rusty keys.   1. _____

2. Where (is, are) the tickets for tonight's game?   2. _____

3. Neither of the girls (like, likes) chocolate.   3. _____

4. One of the kettles (is, are) boiling.   4. _____

5. There (was, were) too many fish in that tank.   5. _____

6. Everyone in our art class (like, likes) working with clay.   6. _____

7. One of those notebooks (is, are) mine.   7. _____

8. Nobody (has, have) lived in that house for years.   8. _____

9. Every ticket for the hockey game (has, have) been sold.   9. _____

10. There (was, were) twenty-five guests at my birthday party.   10. _____

11. (Has, Have) all the plants been watered?   11. _____

12. No one (has, have) seen those tickets.   12. _____

13. When (was, were) the boys expected to arrive?   13. _____

14. There (is, are) two spiders in the cage.   14. _____

15. Where (is, are) the books on space travel?   15. _____

Learning about Suffixes

As you've already learned, a prefix is a word part added to the beginning of a word to change its meaning.

Base Word	Prefix	New Word	New Meaning
healthy	un-	unhealthy	not healthy

A **suffix** is a word part added to the end of a word or another word part. Unlike prefixes, only a few suffixes change the meaning of the base word completely.

Base Word	Suffix	New Word	New Meaning
fear	-less	fearless	without fear

Suffixes are important because they let us use words in different ways. Suffixes such as *-ist, -eer, -er,* and *-or* can be added to certain words to form nouns. These suffixes all mean "a person who does something." Let's look at some examples.

A person who plays the violin is a *violinist.*

Someone in charge of an auction is an *auctioneer.*

A person who plays the drums is a *drummer.*

Someone who studies geology is a *geologist.*

A person who conducts is a *conductor.*

C. Use the words in heavy type to help you complete each of the following. Use a dictionary to check your spelling.

Example:

Someone who draws **cartoons** is a _cartoonist_ .

1. A person who designs and makes **puppets** is a _____ .

2. A person who studies **biology** is a _____ .

3. A person who plays the **flute** is a _____ .

4. **Numismatics** is the study of coins and medals. A person who is an expert in numismatics is called a

   _____ .

5. A _____

   is a person trained in **psychology**.

6. A person trained in **chiropody** is a

   _____ .

7. A person who **sculpts** is a

   _____ .

8. **Cartography** is the making of maps or charts. People who earn their living drawing maps are called mapmakers or _____ .

9. A person who plays the violin is a violinist. Someone who plays the **piano** is a

   _____ .

10. A **timpanist** would probably belong to an _____ .

11. How does a **pessimist** differ from an **optimist**?

    _____

12. What would a **philatelist** collect? _____

13. Someone who plays a musical **accompaniment** for a singer is an _____

14. My sister studied bees at college and now works in an **apiary** as an _____

What would you expect to do in a job as a milliner? Originally, this word was used to describe someone who came from Milan, a city in Italy. People from Milan migrated all over Europe. Many of them opened shops and specialized in the manufacture and sale of women's hats. Before long, anyone who made hats came to be called a "Milaner." Today, people who make and sell women's hats are still called milliners.

D. Here are some more occupations. Use your dictionary to discover what a person in each occupation would do. Be sure to write clear explanations. Saying that a lexicographer is someone skilled in lexicography is not very helpful. Knowing that lexicography refers to making dictionaries, you could write, "A lexicographer is someone who compiles dictionaries."

1. cellist	5. horticulturist	9. ophthalmologist	13. ornithologist
2. meteorologist	6. dermatologist	10. genealogist	14. ventriloquist
3. podiatrist	7. chronologist	11. cosmetologist	15. paleontologist
4. taxidermist	8. orthopedist	12. neurologist	16. phrenologist

For Experts Only

E. a. Use an unabridged dictionary to find the meaning of each of these words. In your notebook, write an interesting sentence using each word.

dendrologist   fabulist   pomologist   aurist

b. How does a somniloquist differ from a somnambulist?

Practising Editing Skills

Animals send and receive messages in fascinating ways. Did you know that grasshoppers hear with their legs or that honeybees "dance" to show others in the hive where nectar can be found? Ants use scent glands on their abdomens to create chemical trails that tell their neighbors where to find food. Male bears mark out their territory by reaching up as high as possible and scratching tree trunks.

F. Imagine you're the editor of a nature magazine for young people aged ten to thirteen. One of your readers has sent in the following article titled " The Language of Dolphins." As you read the article, think about how it could be improved.

Dolphins communicate with a whole series of noises such as squeaks and clicks. Dolphins also use grunts and groans. Dolphins communicate with hisses and whistles, too. Some scientists think dolphins make these sounds by forcing air from small air sacs. The air sacs are in the dolphin's head. The sacs are close to the blowhole.

Dolphins can hear a wide range of low- and high-pitched sounds. They can even hear sounds beyond what humans can hear. Dolphins don't have external ears as we do. Sound enters the dolphin's head through two openings. These openings are behind the dolphin's eyes. The openings are tiny. They are only half a millimetre wide. Scientists still don't know exactly how dolphins hear. They do know they have excellent hearing.

They use these sounds to communicate with other dolphins. They send out a distress signal, for example, when they are in trouble. Other dolphins hear this signal. They begin searching for the animal in trouble. They finally find the injured dolphin. They push it to the surface. They want to help it breathe. They will often remain beside a sick dolphin for weeks. They stay until the sick animal gets well or dies.

1. If you were to edit this article, what changes would you make? Try to think of at least three ways to improve it.

_____

_____

_____

2. The writer of this article used too many short sentences. Find the sentences you think could be combined.

3. Now rewrite the article in your notebook making the following changes.

   a. Join sentences wherever you can.

   b. The writer has overused the word *dolphins* in the first paragraph. When you rewrite this paragraph, try to use the word *dolphins* only in the topic sentence. Use pronouns or the expression *these animals* in place of *dolphins* in the other sentences.

   c. Many of the sentences in the third paragraph begin the same way. When you rewrite, start the second sentence with the words, "When they're in trouble." What other ways could you suggest to introduce sentence variety?

Unit 14

The Comma with Appositives

A word or group of words that follows a noun and tells something about it is called an **appositive**.

> The Klondike, a Yukon River sternwheeler, once carried passengers and freight between Whitehorse and Dawson City.

In this sentence, the appositive *a Yukon River sternwheeler* gives us further information about the noun *Klondike*. Notice that the meaning of the sentence does not change when the appositive is left out. Note also that commas appear before and after the appositive.

A. Underline the appositives in the following sentences. Then reread each sentence leaving out the words you have underlined. The basic meaning of the sentence should not change. Place a comma before and after each appositive.

1. The city of Hamilton a major steel-producing centre in Canada is located at the western end of Lake Ontario.

2. Many people in Prince Edward Island the smallest province in Canada earn their living growing potatoes.

3. British Columbia's Douglas Lake Ranch one of the world's largest working ranches covers 200 000 hectares and has 16 000 head of cattle.

4. Many ships have been wrecked on Sable Island a narrow strip of sand off the east coast of Nova Scotia.

5. Near Churchill a seaport on Hudson Bay northeast of Winnipeg scientists at a rocket research station are trying to learn more about the northern lights.

6. Calgary the centre of Canada's oil industry is in the eastern foothills of the Rocky Mountains.

Combining Sentences with Appositives

You can often use appositives to combine sentences. Let's combine these two sentences.
> One-third of the people in Moncton speak French.
> Moncton is a city in eastern New Brunswick.

To combine the sentences, let's change the second one into an appositive.
> One-third of the people in Moncton, a city in eastern New Brunswick, speak French.

Remember, an appositive must always follow the noun it describes or explains.

B. Read each of the following pairs of sentences carefully. In each case, the second sentence gives further information about a noun in the first sentence. Combine each pair of sentences by making the second sentence into an appositive. Place the appositive directly after the noun it describes. Be sure to punctuate your sentences correctly. You will have to reword some of the sentences.

1. Gander has a huge international airport. The town of Gander is in northeastern Newfoundland.

   _____

   _____

2. Saskatchewan has more farmland than any other province. This province is the greatest wheat-growing region in North America.

   _____

   _____

3. The Montreal Expos play their home games in Olympic Stadium. The Expos are a team in baseball's National League.

   _____

   _____

4. In Inuvik, Our Lady of Victory Church is built in the shape of an igloo and painted white to resemble ice. Inuvik is the largest Canadian community north of the Arctic Circle.

   _____

   _____

5. Daniel Defoe wrote *Robinson Crusoe*. This novel is the story of a sailor marooned on a desert island.

   _____

   _____

6. Antonio Stradivari made some of the finest violins ever produced. He was born in Italy.

   _____

   _____

7. Hummingbirds are the smallest birds in the world. They are the only birds that can fly backward.

   _____

   _____

8. Ospreys live only on fish. These birds are members of the hawk family.

   _____

C. In your notebook, write sentences of your own using each of the following word groups as appositives. Remember to punctuate your sentences correctly.

1. the best gymnast in our school
2. the principal of Maple Grove School
3. my favorite television program
4. the fastest runner on the track team
5. the vegetable I like least
6. the largest city in our province

Adding Suffixes to Words Ending in "Y"

In Unit 13, you learned that a suffix is a word part added to the end of a word (or another word part). Sometimes, adding a suffix changes the spelling of the base word. Notice what happens when suffixes are added to words ending in *y*.

1 If a word ends in *y*, change the *y* to an *i* when adding any suffix except one beginning with *i*.

reply + ed = replied   but   reply + ing = replying

English uses a few one-syllable words that end in a consonant and the letter *y*. Dictionaries often give two spellings for these words when suffixes are added.

dry + er (a machine that dries clothes) may be spelled *dryer* or *drier*

fly + er (a person who flies) may be spelled *flyer* or *flier*

2 Words ending in a vowel + *y* usually keep the *y* when a suffix is added.

play + ed = played   obey + ed = obeyed   joy + ful = joyful

Four exceptions to this rule are:

day + ly = daily   pay + ed = paid   say + ed = said   lay + ed = laid

D. Add the suffixes indicated to make new words.

1. easy + est = _____
2. rely + able = _____
3. betray +ed = _____
4. breezy + est = _____
5. spray + ed = _____
6. clumsy + ness = _____
7. destroy + ing = _____
8. repay + ed = _____

9. mislay + ed = _____
10. speedy + er = _____
11. prepay + ed = _____
12. multiply + ed = _____
13. tiny + est = _____
14. enjoy + able = _____
15. try + ed = _____
16. survey + ing = _____

Using Pronouns Correctly: Part 1

In your community, people work at different jobs. If the pipes in your house begin to leak, you call a plumber. If your teeth are aching, you visit a dentist.

In language, sets of pronouns have different jobs to do as well. Words such as *I*, *he*, and *them* are called **personal pronouns**. The box on the right lists personal pronouns that can be used in the subject position.

Singular	Plural
I	we
you	you
he she it	they

Choosing the right pronoun is usually easy when the subject is singular. The following sentences, for example, probably sound wrong to you.

Me slept in yesterday. Him set a record in the high jump.

Sometimes a pronoun is used with a noun or another pronoun to make a compound subject. When this happens, choosing the correct pronoun is more difficult. Which of these sentences sounds correct to you?

Sharon and me went swimming last night.

Sharon and I went swimming last night.

If you're not sure, read the sentences without the words *Sharon and*. When you do this, you'll quickly realize that *I*, not *me*, is the correct pronoun to use.

E. Write the correct pronouns in the blanks at the right. Test each sentence by reading it without the noun and the word *and*. You may need to change the verb to make it agree.

1. Wes and (he, him) repaired the radio.

1. _____

2. Fiona and (I, me) are working together.

2. _____

3. My brother and (him, he) are on the same team.

3. _____

4. Wendy and (me, I) have piano lessons today.

4. _____

5. Henry, Frank, and (he, him) took the dog for a walk.

5. _____

6. (Them, They) and their friends are often late.

6. _____

7. Peggy and (her, she) always finish first.

7. _____

8. My grandmother and (he, him) went to the football game.

8. _____

9. After the concert, my friends and (they, them) went swimming.

9. _____

10. Manjit and (I, me) found the keys in the parking lot.

10. _____

11. Your brother and (them, they) left yesterday.

11. _____

Sometimes a pronoun is used following a form of the verb *to be*. In informal conversation with your friends, expressions such as "It's me" or "It was us" are quite acceptable. In formal writing, such as essays and letters to important people, always use a subject pronoun after the verb *to be*.

Unit 15

Using Pronouns Correctly: Part 2

In the previous unit, you studied personal pronouns that are used in the subject position: *I, you, he, she, it, we,* and *they.* Personal pronouns sometimes follow an action verb. When this happens you must use an object pronoun.

Subject Pronouns	Object Pronouns
I told Jerry.	Jerry told *me.*
He followed Paula.	Paula followed *him.*
She called Joan.	Joan called *her.*
It saw the boys.	The boys saw *it.*
We invited the principal.	The principal invited *us.*
You met Josie.	Josie met *you.*
They asked their parents.	Their parents asked *them.*

Notice that two of the pronouns, *you* and *it,* do not change form.

Sometimes an action verb is followed by a noun and a pronoun. As with subject pronouns, your ear will usually tell you when to use an object pronoun. Remember to test the sentence by reading it without the noun and the word *and,* like this:

The constant hammering gave Chris and (I, me) a headache.

The constant hammering gave (I, me) a headache.

The constant hammering gave Chris and me a headache.

A. In each of the following sentences, choose the correct pronoun and write it in the blank. Some sentences need object pronouns; others need subject pronouns. Test each sentence by reading it without the noun and the word *and.*

1. The Sullivans asked Gladys and (I, me) to come.

1. _____

2. The searchers found Susan and (she, her) near Hamilton Lake.

2. _____

3. Hank and (I, me) went cross-country skiing.

3. _____

4. The naturalist showed Keith and (I, me) the tarantula.

4. _____

5. My aunt took Ann and (she, her) skin diving.

5. _____

6. The weather forced Tom and (him, he) to come home early.

6. _____

7. Just before sunset, Anna and (she, her) reached the cabin.

7. _____

8. No one told Larry and (I, me).

8. _____

9. Mrs.Neufeld gave Christine and (her, she) the key.

9. _____

10. The fire started after Eric and (I, me) had left.

10. _____

11. Next Saturday, Trudy and (they, them) are going to the Calgary Stampede.

11. _____

12. My grandparents took my cousin and (I, me) to the Ontario Science Centre.

12. _____

B. Decide whether each of the following groups of words contain subject or object pronouns. Then, write interesting sentences of your own using each word group correctly.

1. Michael Marusaki and me _____

_____

2. the volleyball coach and us _____

_____

3. my younger sister and she _____

_____

4. the bus driver and him _____

_____

5. one of the police officers and I _____

_____

6. Jody and her _____

_____

7. a large black dog named Mandy and him _____

_____

8. the captain of the hockey team and he _____

_____

9. Kirsten and them _____

_____

10. the players on the team from Ottawa and we _____

_____

Checking Up on Punctuation

C. Using the proofreading symbols, show where capital letters and commas are needed in these sentences.

1. hay river one of the largest communities in the northwest territories is located on the south shore of great slave lake.

2. takakkaw falls the highest waterfall in canada is in yoho national park.

3. last spring we visited the west edmonton mall the largest shopping centre in north america.

4. gaetan boucher one of the greatest canadian speedskaters was born in charlesbourg quebec on may 10 1958. he won two gold medals at the winter olympics in sarajevo yugoslavia.

5. the niagara river connects lake erie and lake ontario and forms part of the boundary between the province of ontario and the state of new york.

6. potatoes are the leading farm product in new brunswick. farmers also raise barley oats and wheat as well as fruits such as apples blueberries and strawberries.

Using Compound Sentences

In language, the words *and, but,* and *or* are often used to join parts of sentences with each other. Sometimes these words are used to link complete sentences. A word that joins sentences or parts of sentences is called a **conjunction**.

> Much of the world's supply of nickel is mined near Sudbury. Rich iron ore deposits are found in the Algoma district of northeastern Ontario.

> Much of the world's supply of nickel is mined near Sudbury, *and* rich iron ore deposits are found in the Algoma district of northeastern Ontario.

A sentence made up of two complete sentences is called a **compound sentence**. Notice that a comma is used before the conjunction.

Compound sentences are only one of many ways to join ideas. Be careful not to use them too often. Using different kinds of sentences will make your writing livelier and more interesting.

Three important conjunctions used in compound sentences are *and, but,* and *or.*

1. Use *and* when the second sentence gives added information.

> I held the beaker, *and* Steve added the solution.

2. Use *but* when the second sentence gives a contrasting or different idea.

> Laura is going to the hockey game, *but* her brother has to finish his homework.

3. Use *or* when the second sentence gives an alternative or a choice.

> The rain must stop soon, *or* the race will be cancelled.

D. Rewrite each of the following sentence pairs as a compound sentence. Use the conjunctions *and*, *but*, or *or*.

1. Be at our house by three o'clock. Dad will drive us to the hockey game.

   _____

   _____

2. The hungry bear charged into the river. The fish escaped.

   _____

   _____

3. Don't forget to lock that door. The snakes will escape.

   _____

   _____

4. Suddenly the fire alarm rang. Everyone left the building.

   _____

   _____

5. Ray ran as fast as he could. Don won the race.

   _____

   _____

E. Complete each of the following compound sentences. Be sure the two parts of the sentence are closely related.

1. By three o'clock the roads were very icy, and _____

   _____

2. Keep that door closed, or _____

   _____

3. Karla arrived at ten o'clock, but _____

   _____

4. Suddenly the room filled with dense, grey smoke, and _____

   _____

5. The skydiver wanted to land in the lake, but _____

   _____

Expressing an Opinion

Should all students in Canadian schools learn to speak French fluently? Do UFO's exist? All of us have opinions on questions such as these. Your opinion is what you think about a topic. It explains how you feel about people, places, or issues.

Before you form an opinion, try to gather all the information you can on an issue. Check out the evidence. Find out what the experts think. Read magazine articles and books on the subject. Carefully study the arguments on both sides. Once you've researched the issue thoroughly, make up your mind which side is more convincing.

One problem that has always puzzled scientists is the disappearance of the dinosaurs. For nearly 140 million years, these enormous creatures dominated the land. Then, about 65 million years ago, they suddenly died out.

What really happened to the dinosaurs is one of the world's great mysteries. For many years, scientists thought the earth's climate had changed and the world had become cooler. Because dinosaurs could not adapt to the change, they died off. Recently, many scientists have disagreed with this theory. Let's look at the arguments on both sides.

Theory of Changing Climates

Supporting Evidence	Opposing Evidence
• About the time the dinosaurs became extinct, the climate cooled somewhat and may have become too cold for dinosaurs.	• After examining the fossil remains of plants, scientists can find no evidence of a major drop in temperature.
• Dinosaurs are thought to have been reptiles and, therefore, cold-blooded. As the temperature fell, their internal temperature dropped and they died.	• Recently, some scientists have claimed that dinosaurs were warm-blooded like today's mammals and birds.
• Dinosaurs had no fur or feathers to protect them from the cold and were too big to dig holes in the ground for shelter.	• If a change in climate killed the dinosaurs, why didn't other reptiles such as lizards, turtles, and crocodiles die as well?
• Once a reptile as large as a dinosaur had lost its body heat, it would have taken a long time to get it back.	• Climates had changed regularly during the time the dinosaurs lived on earth and they managed to survive these changes.
• As the weather became cooler, much of the vegetation on which the plant-eaters depended could no longer grow and many of these dinosaurs died. Flesh-eating dinosaurs then had nothing to eat.	• Dinosaurs lived all over the world. It is unlikely that a change in climate would have made all regions of the earth unsuitable for them.

F. Before you make up your mind, collect as much information as you can on this topic. Then decide which set of arguments is the most convincing. Using these ideas, write a well-organized article in your notebook persuading others to share your opinion.

Unit 16

Your Ideas Are Important

Why do people smoke? There's no doubt that smoking is a serious risk to health. Scientists now believe that smoking twenty cigarettes a day will shorten a person's life by about five years. Here are some of the other facts they have discovered.

1. Lung cancer is twenty-five times more common in smokers than in people who have never smoked.

2. Tobacco smoke breaks down lung tissues so they cannot properly absorb oxygen. Eventually, this breakdown causes a disease called emphysema.

3. Smoking increases the amounts of fatty substances in the blood. Consequently, the blood thickens and the heart has to work harder to push it around the body.

4. Workers who smoke more than twenty cigarettes a day have to take at least twice as much time off work because of illness as do nonsmokers.

5. Many of the diseases caused by smoking require long periods of expensive hospital care.

6. If a mother smokes while she's pregnant, her baby is likely to be smaller than normal and more apt to have health problems.

7. Second-hand smoke bothers the eyes and noses of sensitive nonsmokers and gives children more respiratory infections.

Should the government ban smoking to protect people from its effects? Should all cigarette advertising be banned? Should smoking be restricted or forbidden on trains, buses, or planes and in other public places? To what extent does the government have the right to interfere with what people do in their own homes?

A. What do you think? Before you decide, talk to some people who smoke. Find out why they continue smoking despite warnings from researchers. How do the smokers you interviewed feel about restricting smoking?

In a democracy, it's important for people to express their opinions. Using the facts about smoking given here, the information you gathered in your interviews, and your own experience, write a letter to the Minister of Health and Welfare in Ottawa. Explain what you think should be done about smoking in Canada.

Using Apostrophes to Show Possession

Nouns that show *who* or *what* something belongs to are called **possessive nouns**. Notice how the apostrophe is used in these examples.

the house belonging to Mr. Clarke	*Mr. Clarke's* house
the dog owned by Emily	*Emily's* dog
the fender of the car	*the car's* fender

The rules for using an apostrophe to show ownership or possession are:

1 To make a singular noun possessive, add an apostrophe followed by an *s*.

My sister's rock collection is on display in the library.

Be careful when you add *'s* to singular nouns ending in *s*. Often the word that is formed is difficult to say because it has too many *s* sounds.

Did you bring *Chris's* umbrella?

With such words, you can form the possessive by simply adding an apostrophe.

Did you bring *Chris'* umbrella?

Either form is acceptable.

2 To make a plural noun ending in *s* possessive, add an apostrophe after the *s*.

The *mechanics'* tools are on the bench. (the tools belonging to the mechanics)

3 To make a plural noun that does not end in *s* possessive, add an apostrophe and *s*.

The *children's* toys were scattered all over the room.

4 When something is owned jointly by two or more people, make only the final noun possessive.

Elaine and Darlene's hamster had babies last night.

B. Rewrite each of the following groups of words using apostrophes.

Example:

the boots of the men   *the men's boots*

1. the sides of the boxes _____

2. the deck of the ship _____

3. the covers of the books _____

4. the dog belonging to Lloyd and Jason _____

5. the smell of the lilies _____

6. the hiss of the snakes _____

7. the notebooks belonging to Phyllis _____

8. the horns of the cows _____

9. the noise of the mice _____

10. the branches of the trees _____

C. Write the correct form of each of the nouns on the left under the proper headings. Use your dictionary if you're not sure of the noun's plural form. Write an interesting sentence in your notebook using each plural possessive form.

Singular	Singular Possessive	Plural	Plural Possessive
woman	woman's	women	women's
1. branch			
2. bus			
3. wife			
4. potato			
5. goose			
6. soldier			
7. army			
8. thief			
9. sheep			
10. calf			

D. Rewrite each of these sentences in your notebook using the correct possessive form of the word in parentheses.

1. Someone stole (Mr.Jones) car from the (teachers) parking lot.
2. Is the blue coat (Shirley) or (Lois)?
3. After a few (hours) delay the boat finally reached (Simpson) Landing.
4. With (Dad) tools and my (brother) advice, I soon repaired the lawnmower.
5. (Alison) sailboat is tied up at (Mr.Chan) wharf.
6. Last (week) hailstorm destroyed my (aunt) cherry crop.
7. My (cousin) wedding announcement is in (Tuesday) paper.
8. Does that store sell (men) and (children) clothing?
9. (Fred) and (Mike) jackets were left on (Ms.Horvath) lawn.
10. The stamp collection is (Anna), but the coin collection is (Hugh).
11. Did you bring the (babies) blankets?
12. Ai Lee hung (Len and Nick) badminton racket in the garage.
13. (Dennis) feet are larger than (Brian).
14. (Margo and Jill) dentist won the hang gliding championship.
15. The (Murphys) alarm went off at midnight.

Checking Up on Pronouns

E. For each of the following sentences, choose the correct form of the pronoun. Write your choice in the blank at the right.

1. Every one of the girls on the volleyball team played (her, their) best.   1. _____

2. Neither of the boys played as well as (he, they) could.   2. _____

3. Will one of your friends loan you (her, their) sleeping bag?   3. _____

4. One of the carpenters left (his, their) hammer on the table.   4. _____

5. Each of the contestants anxiously waited for (her, their) chance to perform.   5. _____

6. Both Norma and Jan brought (her, their) guitars.   6. _____

7. If you see anyone in the gymnasium, please ask (him, them) to leave.   7. _____

8. Everyone must bring (her, their) lunch tomorrow.   8. _____

9. Neither of the new houses had (its, their) walls painted.   9. _____

10. No one should take this course unless (he, they) can speak French fluently.   10. _____

11. Either of the girls can join the band if (she, they) wants to.   11. _____

12. Neither Bret nor his brother brought (his, their) skis.   12. _____

What Am I Studying?

Words ending in the suffix -*logy* may look more difficult than they really are. The meaning of these words is easy if you remember that -*logy* means "the study of." Criminology is the study of crime and criminals. Mineralogy is the study of minerals. What would you expect to study in a course on Egyptology?

F. What would you be learning about if you studied these subjects? Check those you are not sure of in your dictionary.

1. zoology _____

2. geology _____

3. ichthyology _____

4. herpetology _____

5. entomology _____

6. ornithology _____

7. toxicology _____

8. gerontology _____

9. meteorology _____

10. biology _____

Checking Up on Combining Sentences

You have now learned three ways to combine sentences:

1. Turn one of the sentences into an appositive.

> Robert Service lived in a log cabin on the hillside above Dawson City. Service wrote many poems about the Yukon gold rush.

> Robert Service, a poet who wrote about the Yukon gold rush, lived in a log cabin on the hillside above Dawson City.

2. Use a compound subject or a compound predicate.

> Ospreys, bald eagles, and turkey vultures inhabit Manitoba's Riding Mountain National Park.

3. Use a compound sentence.

> Reg washed the dishes. Norm dried them.

> Reg washed the dishes, and Norm dried them.

G. Combine each of the following groups of sentences. With some pairs you can use an appositive. With others a compound subject, a compound predicate, or a compound sentence will be needed. Leave out any unnecessary words. Write your sentences in your notebook.

1. The Bruce Trail joins Queenston near Niagara Falls and Tobermory at the tip of the Bruce Peninsula. This trail is Canada's longest hiking trail.

2. Halifax is one of Canada's most important ports. It is the capital of Nova Scotia. Halifax is the largest city in Atlantic Canada.

3. Arctic foxes and arctic hares inhabit Auyuittuq National Park. Polar bears live here also. This park is Canada's first national park north of the Arctic Circle.

4. Swift Current is on the main line of the Canadian Pacific Railway. It is a city in southwestern Saskatchewan.

5. While in Vancouver, we visited Stanley Park and Gastown. We also went to the Nitobe Memorial Garden. This garden is on the campus of the University of British Columbia.

6. Ontario was first settled by farmers. Today, most people live in cities.

7. Saint John's is closer to Europe than any other major North American city. It is the capital of and largest city in Newfoundland.

8. The Saint Lawrence River links the Atlantic Ocean with the Great Lakes. The Saint Lawrence is the second longest river in North America.

Unit 17

Using Apostrophes with Contractions

A **contraction** is two words shortened into one. The word "contraction" comes from the verb *contract* meaning to "shrink" or "make smaller." Let's look at some examples.

he + had = he'd   she + will = she'll   we + would = we'd

Notice that the apostrophe takes the place of the missing letter or letters.

Contractions are often used to join a verb with the word *not*. Usually you simply shorten *not* to *n't* and join it to the verb.

are + not = aren't   were + not = weren't   is + not = isn't

Two exceptions to this rule are:

can + not = can't   will + not = won't

Contractions are also used to join a pronoun with forms of the verbs *to be* and *to have*.

he + is = he's   I + have = I've

In these contractions, replace the first letter or letters of the verb with an apostrophe.

A. Rewrite each of the following sentences in your notebook. Use contractions wherever you can.

1. I would do it but I cannot leave.

2. Are you not going to tell Mrs.Suddaby that Sally will not be coming to choir practice?

3. Kim's mother phoned to say she would be late.

4. I would rather they would come at six o'clock.

5. Ben would have been here on time if the bus had not been late.

6. You have told some unusual stories, Wally, but this one is the strangest tale I have ever heard.

Four Problem Pairs

Because they sound alike, the pairs of words in the table at the right are often confused. Remember that possessive pronouns show ownership. They do not need an apostrophe. Contractions, however, are shortened forms of two words. They need an apostrophe to show that a letter or letters have been left out.

Possessive Pronouns	Contractions
its tongue	it's = it is
your softball	you're = you are
their garden	they're = they are
whose truck	who's = who is

B. Write the correct word from each set of parentheses in the blank at right.

1. (Their, They're) team lost all (its, it's) games.

2. Do you know (who's, whose) here?

3. (Their, They're) going to meet us near (your, you're) uncle's farm.

4. (Their, They're) planning to use (they're, their) father's tools.

5. (It's, Its) certainly a shame the horse broke (it's, its) leg.

6. (Whose, Who's) car is parked in (they're, their) driveway?

7. I think (they're, their) going with (they're, their) grandparents.

8. (It's, Its) not (you're, your) fault.

9. (Whose, Who's) (you're, your) new friend?

10. If (it's, its) sunny on Tuesday, (they're, their) planning to go hiking.

1. _____

2. _____

3. _____

4. _____

5. _____

6. _____

7. _____

8. _____

9. _____

10. _____

Adjectives: Words that Go with Nouns

A sentence made up mainly of nouns and verbs gives us only the basic facts. Let's look at an example.

The elephant crossed the plain.

This sentence could be made more interesting by adding words to describe the nouns.

The *weary* elephant crossed the *parched, rocky* plain.

The *magnificent bull* elephant crossed the *grassy* plain.

Words that describe nouns or pronouns are called **adjectives**. Adjectives do more than describe, however. They also make the noun's meaning more exact. Notice how the adjectives added to the example sentence bring to mind a clearer picture of the elephant and its surroundings.

Sometimes adjectives are said to "modify" nouns. The word **modify** means "to change in some way." By carefully adding adjectives, writers can change or modify the images their words create in their readers' minds. The noun *dog*, for example, suggests a barking animal with four legs. Everyone reading this noun will imagine a different dog. Notice how the picture of the dog changes as adjectives are added.

a shaggy, black dog   a large, vicious dog   a hunting dog

Adjectives modify nouns by pointing out:

1. *What kind?*   the *blue* truck, a *large* egg, some *torn* pages, my *broken* arm
2. *How many?*   *eight* kittens, *several* farmers
3. *How much?*   *more* salt, *less* sugar, *some* onions
4. *Which one?*   *this* ladder, *that* bucket, *these* children, *those* tractors
5. *Whose?*   *your* socks, *her* uniform, *their* car

Generally, adjectives come before the noun they describe. They also follow forms of the verb *to be* and verbs such as *seem, become, feel, look, taste,* and *smell*.

This orange is *juicy*.   Those watermelons look *ripe*.

That pie smells *delicious*.   His hand felt *cold*.

Sometimes writers purposely place adjectives after the noun to make them stand out.

The clouds, *dark* and *stormy*, filled the mountain valley.

Good writers take a keen interest in words. When you're reading, watch for examples of the effective use of adjectives.

C. Circle the adjectives in each of the following sentences. Draw an arrow from the adjective to the noun it describes or modifies. You should find twenty-one adjectives.

Example:

Zebras have (large) heads and a (short), (stiff) mane.

1. The potto is a small animal living in

   western Africa.

2. Lion cubs are blind and helpless at birth.

3. The powerful gorilla had huge shoulders and a broad chest.

4. Most parrots have thick, hooked bills and bright feathers.

5. A hard shell covers the entire body of the lobster.

6. Pronghorn antelope have large ears, slender legs, and short tails.

7. The jaws of an alligator are strong and have many sharp teeth.

Choosing Adjectives Carefully

Well-chosen adjectives add sparkle and vitality to your writing. Always try to use adjectives that describe exactly what you want the reader to imagine.

D. Use the thesaurus at the back of this book to find three specific adjectives for each of these general adjectives. Be sure you know the meaning of each of the words you select.

big   important   unhappy   smart   good   hot

E. Write at least four adjectives that could be used to describe each of the following people. Take time to choose carefully. Do not use the same adjective more than once. Circle the adjective in each set that you think is the most descriptive.

Example:

Seven guests trapped on the roof of a hotel by a raging fire

terrified, scared, petrified, frightened

1. A hockey coach whose team has just won an Olympic gold medal

2. The pilot of a jumbo jet whose plane has just run out of fuel at 10 000 metres

3. Your classmates if the principal suddenly announced that the summer holidays would be two weeks shorter than usual

4. A young pianist playing her first concert with the Toronto Symphony Orchestra

5. An elderly man chasing a stray chicken around his garden

F. Rewrite these sentences in your notebook. Replace the general nouns in heavy type with more exact words. Add one or two carefully selected adjectives to describe each of the nouns in italics.

1. Put the **vegetables** in the *bag*.
2. The *truck* thundered down the *hill* and crashed into the **building**.
3. The **dishes** are on the *table* with the **dessert**.
4. Lorne found the **treasure** hidden in a *box* under the *cabin*.

Blue Moons and Green Thumbs

Many common expressions in English use color adjectives. If something happens only "once in a blue moon," for example, it takes place rarely. People are said to have "green thumbs" if they are successful gardeners.

G. Use your dictionary to find the meaning of each of these phrases. Write the meanings in your notebook.

1. a white lie
2. a round robin schedule
3. a square deal
4. a white elephant
5. the black sheep of the family
6. grey matter

Unit 18

Synonyms: Words with Similar Meanings

A word that has almost the same meaning as another word is called a **synonym**. "Large" is a synonym of "big." "Powerful" is a synonym of "strong."

Often, writers use a dictionary of synonyms called a **thesaurus** to help them in their work. The word *thesaurus* is a Latin word meaning "treasure." A thesaurus is a treasure chest of synonyms and antonyms.

A thesaurus is particularly useful when you edit your work. Sometimes you'll need a synonym to avoid repeating the same word. This book can also help you find words to make your ideas clear and precise. You'll find a mini-thesaurus at the back of this book.

A. As in a dictionary, the words listed in bold type in a thesaurus are called **entry words**. Following each entry word is a list of synonyms. Remember that these words may not all have exactly the same meaning. Let's look at an example.

angry, annoyed, berserk, cross, displeased, enraged, furious, impatient, incensed, inflamed, irate, irritated, peeved, raging, upset, vexed

All these words refer to different levels of anger. For instance, someone who is berserk is exceptionally upset and can become violent and destructive. In Norse mythology, Berserk was a fierce fighter who could take the form of wild beasts and could not be harmed by fire or iron. By contrast, someone who is annoyed is only mildly upset. Flies might annoy horses.

1. List four synonyms for *angry* that mean "greatly upset."

_____

2. List four synonyms for *angry* that mean "mildly upset."

_____

Never use an unfamiliar synonym from the thesaurus before checking its exact meaning in the dictionary. A strange word that you hope will impress your readers may be unsuitable in certain situations.

B. Each of the following entry words is followed by two synonyms in parentheses. The meaning of the words in parentheses is similar but not identical. Look up each word in the dictionary. In the blanks following each pair, explain how the meanings of the words in parentheses differ. Then, in your notebook, use each word in an interesting sentence of your own.

Example:

broken (cracked — smashed)

cracked — broken but not completely apart.

smashed — broken into pieces.

1. **special** (peculiar — unique)

2. **frightened** (panicky — petrified)

3. **dirty** (dusty — grimy)

4. **soft** (downy — fleecy)

5. **weak** (flimsy — fragile)

6. **new** (modern — novel)

7. **brave** (intrepid — martial)

8. **clear** (transparent — translucent)

Being Alert to What Words Suggest

The exact definition of a word is called its **denotation**. The Canadian Intermediate Dictionary defines a snake as "a reptile with an elongated body, scaly skin, and no legs, eyelids, or extended ears."

Many people fear and dislike snakes. When they hear the word *snake*, they feel uncomfortable, imagining a peculiar, dangerous animal. Because no two people are alike, a word never means exactly the same thing to two people.

The thoughts and feelings that a word arouses are known as its **connotation**. The word *connote* means "to suggest or to imply." Your uncle would probably not object to being referred to as "tall and well-built," for example, but might well get upset if you called him "big and fat." The words *stubborn*, *obstinate*, and *pigheaded* all mean "not giving" or "not yielding." *Obstinate*, however, often suggests being unreasonable in refusing to give in, while *pigheaded* implies that someone is stupidly stubborn.

C. Writers often choose words with particular connotations to create a certain atmosphere. The following paragraph is from the novel *King of the Wind*. As you read the paragraph, notice how the author describes the many smells the character experiences.

> The world was full of wonders! If he stretched his nostrils to the wind, he could sift the most interesting smells — the delicious fragrance of clover, the biting smell of smoke from the burning stubble of cornfields, the perfume from orange and lime groves, the spicy aroma of pine woods beyond the city wall, the musky smell of wild boar, the cool, moisture-laden scent of the clouds that blew over the snow-topped mountains. He could not label the smells as yet, but he was sorting them out in his mind.

Marguerite Henry, *King of the Wind*

1. Underline the words used to describe smells in this paragraph.

2. Why would the author describe the clover as having a "*delicious* fragrance" while the stubble has a "*biting* smell"?

   _____

   _____

3. Look at the words used to describe the orange and lime groves, the pine woods, the wild boar, and the clouds. What impression did the author hope to create in using these words?

   _____

4. What feelings about the scene do the descriptive words connote?

   _____

5. List three synonyms for the word *smell* that have an unfavorable connotation.

   _____

D. Look up each of the following adjectives in your dictionary. Circle the word with the most positive connotation. Write sentences in your notebook showing clearly the meaning of each of these words.

1. famous - notorious
2. immature - young
3. plump - fat
4. rotten - overripe
5. senile - forgetful
6. proud - arrogant
7. sly - clever
8. slender - skinny

Creating Word Pictures

A **description** is a word picture explaining how something looks, feels, or acts. Good description should create in the reader's imagination what the writer wants to be seen, heard, and felt. Many descriptions start with a general statement. Often, this statement explains how the writer feels about what is being described. A series of details usually follows to explain why the writer feels this way. As these details appeal to the senses, they are called **sensory details**. By carefully choosing sensory details, the writer tries to bring the story to life in the reader's mind.

E. Let's look at an example. Here is R.D. Lawrence's description of a bull moose trapped by a pack of wolves.

> The bull moose stood like some prehistoric creature poised for battle. He stood seven feet high at the shoulder, all four legs planted firmly, the snow reaching halfway to his knees. His long neck was outstretched, his spear-shaped ears were flattened to the sides of his head. From the bulbous nose spurted twin jets of snorted breath, forming clouds of vapor in the frigid air. He was big and dangerous, a giant of the forest with black, wiry mane erect over his humped shoulders and along his neck, ending just short of his antler bosses. He stood in a birch thicket, defiant, unmoving. He would not run from the pack.

R.D. Lawrence, *Cry Wild*

1. What overall impression of the bull moose does the novelist create?

   _____

2. List six sensory details Lawrence uses to support this impression.

   a. _____

   b. _____

   c. _____

   d. _____

   e. _____

   f. _____

3. List four words that suggest the moose will be a fierce opponent.

   _____

F. Now it's your turn to try writing a description. Decide which of the following topics you would like to write about and underline your choice.

1. A school cafeteria at noon
2. A creature in a science fiction movie
3. A crowded beach on a hot summer afternoon
4. A busy airport terminal forced to close because of a sudden snowstorm
5. Bargain day in a department store
6. The car of the future

Decide what overall impression you want to create about your topic. If you selected the science fiction creature, for example, will your creature be friendly or hostile? Write about the impression you intend to create on the following line.

_____

List five sensory details that will help create your overall impression.

a. _____

b. _____

c. _____

d. _____

e. _____

f. _____

Now write a descriptive paragraph in your notebook. Start with a topic sentence that gives the overall impression. Choose your adjectives carefully. Be aware of both the denotation and the connotation of your words.

Unit 19

Choosing Details to Build Mood

The word *mood* means "the way you feel at a certain time." Our moods often change. Learning you received a perfect score on a science test would probably put you in a good mood. What events could make your mood change to one of sadness?

In writing descriptions, always be aware of the mood you want to create. Before describing someone or something, decide if you want your reader to feel attracted to or repelled by the subject. Once you decide on the mood you want to build, carefully choose the words and sensory details that will help produce that feeling.

Let's look at John Steinbeck's description of a spring afternoon.

> The afternoon was green and gold with spring. Underneath the spread branches of the oaks the plants grew pale and tall, and on the hills the feed was smooth and thick. The sagebrushes shone with new silver leaves and the oaks wore hoods of golden green. Over the hills there hung such a green odor that the horses on the flats galloped madly, and then stopped, wondering; lambs, and even old sheep jumped in the air unexpectedly and landed on stiff legs and went on eating; young clumsy calves butted their heads together and drew back and butted again.

John Steinbeck, *The Red Pony*

A. By carefully selecting details, Steinbeck has created a mood of life and vitality.

1. Read the paragraph again carefully. Underline all the words and phrases that make the scene seem alive and joyful.

2. What colors does the novelist use in describing this scene? Why do you think he chose these colors?

_____

3. Notice that the plants are growing *pale and tall* and the feed *smooth and thick*. What other details tell you the plants are thriving?

_____

4. The author's description of the animals' actions also suggests energy and enjoyment. List three phrases that show the animals are active on this afternoon.

  a. _____

  b. _____

  c. _____

B. Suppose you wanted to write a description of an area near your home on a cold, damp November morning. Before you begin, close your eyes and try to visualize the scene in your mind. Then use the following outline to help plan your paragraph.

1. What colors would you use to describe the scene? Be as specific as possible.

_____

2. In your notebook list six details you could use to help the reader feel the mood you want to establish. Make your details as exact as you can. Now write the paragraph in your notebook. Be sure to start with a topic sentence that sets the mood you want the reader to feel.

Adverbs: Words that Go with Verbs

Adverbs are like adjectives in that they modify or describe other words in a sentence. Most often they add to the meaning of a verb. They answer the questions "Where?" "When?" and "How?"

Arlene parked the car **there**.

(the adverb _there_ tells _where_ she parked)

Arlene parked the car **yesterday**.

(the adverb _yesterday_ tells _when_ she parked)

Arlene parked the car **carefully**.

(the adverb _carefully_ tells _how_ she parked)

Adverbs are usually formed by adding the suffix -_ly_ to an adjective.

Adjective	Adverb
a _quiet_ lake	The dog sat _quietly_.
a _sudden_ bang	The bus stopped _suddenly_.
an _angry_ dog	Lois spoke _angrily_.

Notice that the spelling sometimes changes. For adjectives ending in _y_, for example, change the _y_ to _i_ before adding -_ly_.

Just because a word ends in -_ly_, however, does not guarantee it is an adverb. A few adjectives, such as _lonely_ (the lonely sea), _silly_ (a silly story), _daily_ (a daily paper), and _friendly_ (the friendly raccoon), also end in -_ly_. Also, many common adverbs such as _soon, here, sometime, often_, and _always_ do not end in -_ly_.

Adverbs do not have a set position in a sentence. Usually they can be moved without changing the meaning of the sentence.

Suddenly the runner tripped.

The runner _suddenly_ tripped.

The runner tripped _suddenly_.

Sometimes, however, the position of the adverb does make a difference. How do the following sentences differ in meaning?

Happily, she did not die.

She did not die _happily_.

C. Circle the verbs in each of the following sentences. Underline the adverbs. The number in parentheses tells how many adverbs there are in each sentence. Above each adverb, write the question the adverb answers.

Example:

when

Simone often (takes) pictures at school games. (1)

1. We looked everywhere for Mr.Jorganson's keys. (1)

2. Often the two eagles hunted together. (2)

3. There goes the pilot now. (2)

4. He walked painfully across the room and suddenly collapsed. (2)

5. Sometimes the river rises fast and rapidly floods the town. (3)

6. The boys arrived home early. (2)

7. Soon the young leopards will hunt skilfully. (2)

8. A cactus plant grows slowly and seldom needs water. (2)

9. Then Mary cautiously opened the window and crawled inside. (3)

10. Yesterday our cat brought a large rat home. (2)

Be Careful with Good and Well

Two words often used incorrectly in English are *good* and *well*. **Well** is used as an adverb to tell how something is done.

Be sure to mix the paint **well** before using it.

Well may also be used as an adjective to mean "in good health."

When the hockey game ended, Wendy didn't feel **well**.

Good is always an adjective and should never be used as an adverb.

We had a **good** time at Wayne's birthday party.

Remember that verbs such as *look, feel, taste, seem, smell, sound*, and all parts of the verb *to be* are often followed by adjectives.

That pumpkin pie sure tastes **good**.

My little sister was **good** while my parents were away.

D. Fill in each blank with *good* or *well*.

1. That milk doesn't smell _____ .

2. I am quite _____ , thank you.

3. It is _____ you arrived when you did.

4. Tracy is a _____ gymnast.

5. He and Scott play _____ together.

6. I couldn't do a _____ job of cutting the grass as the lawnmower

   wasn't working _____ .

7. After eating the mince pie, Kim didn't feel _____ .

8. That skirt goes _____ with your new sweater.

Adjective or Adverb?

E. Some words can be used as either an adjective or an adverb. In each of the following sentences, decide if the italicized word is an adjective or an adverb. Explain the reason for your choice on the line following the sentence.

Example:

Because of the drought the river is *low* this year.

adjective - describes the river

The three planes flew *low* over the battlefield.

adverb - tells where the plane flew

1. The prospectors dug *deep* into the hill in search of gold.

   _____

2. "Take a *deep* breath," said the doctor.

   _____

3. You'll probably find the cattle on the *far* side of the hill.

   _____

4. The hikers scrambled *far* up the mountain.

   _____

5. Unfortunately, Kerry's answer was *wrong*.

   _____

6. Everything went *wrong* today.

   _____

7. The first three problems are *hard*.

   _____

8. Last night it rained *hard* for three hours.

9. My mother is always telling me to stand up *straight*.

10. Walk in a *straight* line until you reach that tall pine tree.

Checking Up on Punctuation

F. Punctuate the following sentences correctly. Draw three lines under all letters that should be capitalized.

Example:

<u>e</u>lephants, the largest land animals, feed on grass, shrubs, leaves, roots, bark, and water plants.

1. the badger has a stocky body shaggy hair strong claws and sharp teeth

2. the wart hog an african pig with long curved tusks lives in dry sandy country from southern africa to ethiopia

3. because of their tameness their ability to imitate and their eagerness to learn sea lions are easy to train

4. bernadettes dog a lively irish terrier won first prize

5. the armadillos best protection is its hard stiff shell if threatened it may burrow run away from or claw an attacker

6. flies mosquitoes and other insects cant bite an elephant because its skin is so thick

7. the wolverine one of the largest members of the weasel family has been found as far north as ellesmere island in the arctic

8. the polar bears diet is mostly meat but also includes mushrooms crowberries and sea birds eggs

Unit 20

Adverbs as Intensifiers

Let's imagine you spent yesterday fishing. Depending on how much you wanted to impress your friends, you could tell them about your catch in various ways. You might say:

>I caught a fish yesterday.

Your listener, however, has no idea of the size of the fish. You can solve that problem by adding an adjective:

>I caught a **large** fish yesterday.

But suppose you *really* wanted to impress people with the size of your fish. In that case you could say:

>I caught a **particularly** large fish yesterday. *or*

>I caught a **really** large fish yesterday. *or*

>I caught an **exceptionally** large fish yesterday.

Notice how the words *really*, *particularly*, and *exceptionally* change or modify the meaning of the adjective *large*. Words used to modify adjectives in this way belong to a special group of adverbs called **intensifiers**. Intensifiers modify not only adjectives but also other adverbs. Here are two examples:

>Roger walked *quite* slowly.

>Nancy often talks *too* fast.

Spotting adverbs used as intensifiers is not difficult if you remember these tips:

1 Unlike other adverbs, intensifiers always come before the adjective or adverb they modify.

>*unusually* young   *too* quickly   *rather* fat

2 Intensifiers always answer the question "*How?*"

>How intelligent?   *reasonably* intelligent

>How old?   *extremely* old

A. Each of the following sentences contains an adverb used as an intensifier. Circle the intensifier and draw an arrow to the word it modifies. If the modified word is an adjective, write *Adj* below it. If it is an adverb, write *Adv* below it.

Example:

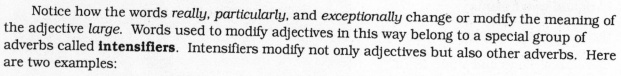

The snow on the driveway is (rather) deep.
                             Adj.

1. Scrambling up the rocks to the glacier was very difficult.

2. The team from Willowdale School arrived quite early.

3. The rain came too late to save the crops.

4. Liza Barclay said her mother felt much better.

5. The crow is an exceptionally clever bird.

6. Are the directions quite clear?

7. Our volleyball team played amazingly well.

8. My grandmother's car is almost new.

9. Don't work too hard.

10. Our dog stays outside except when the weather is very cold.

Writing Concise Sentences

Good writing is concise. The word *concise* means "saying much in a few words." Using fewer words saves your reader time and makes your ideas easier to understand. Here are four ways to make your writing more concise.

1 Where possible, combine shorter sentences.

> During our visit to Kenora, we went for a cruise on Lake of the Woods. Kenora is a town in northern Ontario.

> During our visit to Kenora, a town in northern Ontario, we went for a cruise on Lake of the Woods.

2 Leave out unnecessary words or ideas.

> It was about ten minutes later that a police car came to a stop in front of our house.

> About ten minutes later a police car stopped in front of our house.

3 Don't use adjectives that are synonyms to describe the same noun.

> Suddenly the enormous, huge rhinoceros charged the photographers.

> Because the words *enormous* and *huge* are synonyms, only one is necessary.

4 Do not use a double subject.

> My sister she works as a veterinarian in Charlottetown, Prince Edward Island.

Because this sentence already has a subject, the noun *sister*, the pronoun *she* is not needed.

> My sister works as a veterinarian in Charlottetown, Prince Edward Island.

When you edit, pause after each sentence. Ask yourself these questions:

1. Exactly what did I want to say in this sentence?
2. Will my reader understand my ideas quickly and easily?
3. Have I explained my ideas in as few words as possible?

B. Each of these sentences has unnecessary words. Rewrite each sentence in your notebook. Leave out as many words as you can without changing the meaning. Be ready to explain why the words you took out are not needed.

1. It was in 1988 that the two twins won the trophy.

2. My father he is at a conference in the city of Toronto at the present time.

3. Kangaroos have pouches in which to carry their young in.

4. In my opinion I think that we should be home by nine p.m. in the evening.

5. The snow leopard is a leopard that is native to Tibet.

6. At bingo last night, my grandfather he met up with two old friends that he knew from the Ukraine.

7. The steep, sheer cliffs of Thunderbolt Mountain rose straight up from the calm, quiet surface of Minto Lake.

8. Our school is in need of painting.

9. During the time that we were in Blacks Harbour we paid a visit to a large sardine cannery. Blacks Harbour is a fishing village on the Bay of Fundy.

10. In this book it explains how to write your own autobiography.

Writing a Friendly Letter

You can communicate with friends in many ways. You probably talk to some every day. Others you keep in touch with by telephone. Some of your friends, however, may live far away. The best way to communicate with them is by letter. A friendly letter has five parts:

1. **The Heading**   In this section, put your return address and the date. Notice that your name does not appear in the heading.

2. **The Salutation**   The salutation is your "hello" to the person to whom you are writing. Use a comma after the salutation.

3. **The Body**   In this section, include the news and information you want to pass on to your friend.

4. **The Closing**   At the end of a conversation, you often say "See you later" or "Bye." In a letter, you can use expressions such as *With love, Sincerely, As always,* or *Your friend.* Notice that the first word in the closing is always capitalized.

5. **The Signature**   The signature tells who the letter is from. Make sure it can be easily read.

Let's look at an example.

67 Woodglen Way, SW
Calgary, Alberta
T2W 4H9
May 23, 1989

Dear Brenda,

Last night my parents had a great idea.
Mom and Dad are both working in July and
I'll be on my own. They suggested I invite a
friend to spend the month with me. They're
even willing to pay the air fare to Calgary.
Would you be able to come?

Don't worry about where you'll sleep. I'll
move the guest room bed into my room. That
way we can talk as late as we want. Making
our own lunches will be great fun. I sure
hope you like pizza. I've got a fantastic
recipe!

Calgary is a terrific place to spend the
summer. The sun shines almost every day,
and there's so much to do. During the second
week of July, we could go to the Stampede.
There's calf roping, steer wrestling, barrel
racing, and of course the chuckwagon races.
Prehistoric Park on St. George's Island has
fifty-three life-sized dinosaurs! Can you
imagine? Actually, they're all made of
fiberglass and are quite harmless. Our zoo is
the second largest in Canada and has over

1400 species of animals and birds. If we get bored we can always go to the water slide park or go riding at a guest ranch near the city.

I do hope you're able to come as I'm sure we'll have a great time. This is the first time my parents have ever let me do anything this exciting. Please write soon and let me know when you'll arrive, your flight number, and how long you can stay.

Complimentary closing
(line up with the date, use a comma, capitalize first word)

Your friend,

Marcia

Signature
(sign your name clearly)

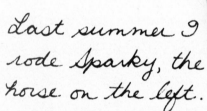

Last summer I rode Sparky, the horse on the left.

C. Using Marcia's letter as a model, write a letter to a friend inviting him or her to visit your community. Use the following plan to help you organize your letter.

Paragraph 1	Following a short introduction, invite your friend to spend some time with you.
Paragraph 2	Give your friend some idea of what life at your home will be like.
Paragraph 3	Give four or five examples of interesting things to do in your community.
Paragraph 4	Conclude your letter. Be sure to ask for any information you feel that you need.

Unit 21

Writing an Exchange Letter

Writing to a person who lives in another country can be both interesting and educational. You could discover, for example, what it's like to live in a small fishing village in Iceland, on a sheep ranch in New Zealand, in a high-rise apartment building in New York City, or in a mining town in West Germany. From an Australian, you could learn about *Tasmanian devils, dugongs, the outback,* and *Australian Rules Football,* while a student in Scotland could explain *chanters, haggis,* and the *Loch Ness Monster.*

A. Write to someone who doesn't live in your area. In your first letter include interesting details about you, your school, and your community. Divide your letter into three parts. Each part should have its own paragraph.

Part One: Yourself

Begin by telling your reader how old you are and where and with whom you live. Then go on to discuss your pets, hobbies, interests, and activities. You might also talk about your friends and relatives.

Part Two: Your School

Mention your grade and discuss the subjects you study and the activities you are involved in at school.

Part Three: Your Community

Mention the places and activities in your community that a visitor would find interesting.

Comparison of Adjectives and Adverbs

In our library there are many *quiet* places to study. Near the windows is *quieter* than by the staircase. The *quietest* place of all, however, is in the far corner.

When you point out how things are alike or different, you are making **comparisons**. Most adjectives and adverbs have different forms to show comparison. Use the **comparative** form (quieter) when you compare only two people, places, or things. For three or more items, however, use the **superlative** form (quietest).

Adjectives and adverbs are compared in one of three ways.

1 Most one-syllable adjectives and adverbs use *-er* and *-est* in comparisons.

		Comparative Form	Superlative Form
Adjective	small	smaller	smallest
Adverb	fast	faster	fastest

2 Most adjectives and adverbs of two or more syllables use *more* or *most* in comparisons.

		Comparative Form	Superlative Form
Adjective	beautiful	more beautiful	most beautiful
Adverb	carelessly	more carelessly	most carelessly

3 A few adjectives and adverbs are irregular:

		Comparative Form	Superlative Form
Adjective	many	more	most
Adverb	much	more	most
Adjective	good	better	best
Adverb	well	better	best
Adjective	bad	worse	worst
Adverb	badly	worse	worst
Adjective	little	less	least
Adverb	far	furthest	furthest

Because of their meaning, some adjectives, such as *dead, square,* and *exact,* cannot be compared. Logically, if something is dead, square, or exact, it cannot become more *dead, square,* or *exact.*

B. Write the comparative and superlative forms of each of the following adjectives and adverbs. Check in your dictionary the spelling of any words you are unsure of. Remember, some adjectives have only one form.

	Comparative Form	Superlative Form
Example: tidy	*tidier*	*tidiest*
1. kind		
2. careful		
3. much		
4. thin		
5. happy		
6. complete		
7. quietly		
8. good		
9. soon		
10. perfect		

C. In each of the following sentences, circle the correct form of the adjective or adverb in parentheses. On the line below each sentence, explain the reason for your choice.

Example:
Trudy is the (taller, ~~tallest~~) player on the basketball team.

more than two players are being compared

1. Tuesday was the (wetter, wettest) day of the month.

_____

_____

2. Which of these two books is the (better, best)?

_____

_____

3. Rob is the (faster, fastest) runner on our relay team.

_____

4. This is the (shadier, shadiest) side of the street.

_____

5. I think Heidi is the (hungrier, hungriest) of the triplets.

_____

6. He is certainly the (more, most) careless person I know.

_____

7. Which of the two movies did you find the (more exciting, most exciting)?

_____

8. Who is (older, oldest), Len or James?

_____

9. Which will live (longer, longest), a bullfrog or a turtle?

_____

10. Of the three girls, Irene has the (better, best) chance of winning.

_____

Using Adverbs Correctly

Here are three tips to remember when using adverbs.

1 Don't use an adjective when an adverb is needed.

    Wrong   Each question you answer correct is worth five marks.

    Right   Each question you answer correctly is worth five marks.

2 Avoid using two negatives together. Most negative words, such as *not, no, never, nothing,* and *none,* begin with the letter *n*. Remember that *n't* is the contraction for *not*. The words *hardly, scarcely,* and *only* are also negatives.

    Wrong   There isn't no more milk in the jug.

    Right   There isn't any more milk in the jug.

3 Don't add the letter *s* to adverbs such as *somewhere, anywhere,* or *nowhere.*

    Wrong   I'm sure your sweater is somewheres in your room.

    Right   I'm sure your sweater is somewhere in your room.

D. Eight of these sentences contain adverb mistakes. Circle the two correct sentences. Rewrite the others in your notebook correcting the errors. Be ready to explain your answers.

1. We didn't see nobody go into the room.

2. Although my mother spoke calm, I knew she was upset.

3. Because of the dense fog, we couldn't see nothing.

4. I hope you aren't hurt bad.

5. Ruth spoke too quietly and we couldn't hear her answers.

6. My sister ran real fast and won the race.

7. I don't know hardly anyone on that team.

8. Don't we have some chocolate ice cream in the freezer?

9. I couldn't find a picture of tyrannosaurus rex anywheres.

10. After eating the apple pie, he didn't feel too good.

Homonyms: Write Them Right

Homonyms are words that sound alike but are spelled differently and have different meanings. The words *steal* and *steel* are homonyms. The word "homonym" comes from two Greek words: *homos*, meaning "same," and *onyma*, meaning "name."

E. Cross out the incorrect homonym in each of these sentences. In your notebook, write your own sentence using each crossed out homonym correctly. Use your dictionary to check any words you're not sure of.

Example:
Be sure to leave the (gate, ~~gait~~) unlocked.

1. Use that bucket to (bail, bale) out the canoe.

2. My father sings (base, bass) in the church choir.

3. Shane challenged the stranger to a (duel, dual) to settle the argument.

4. Your (heart, hart) is about the size of your fist.

5. The geologists found a (vain, vein) of copper on Mount Christy.

6. The police found the (lute, loot) from the bank robbery in the briefcase.

7. In some provinces, a (minor, miner) is anyone eighteen or younger.

8. The teacher told us to stand up (straight, strait).

9. Through a hole in the clouds, we caught (site, sight) of the jumbo jet.

10. Could you (sew, sow) on this button for me?

Unit 22

Homonym Puzzles

A. In this exercise, each definition is followed by a homonym clue. Use this clue to help you find the missing homonym. Write your answer in the spaces at the right. Make sure each space contains only one letter.

Example:

A place to sleep on a train. It sounds like *birth*.

B E R T H

1. A male pig. It sounds like *bore*.

1. _ _ _ _

2. An officer in the army. It sounds like *kernel*.

2. _ _ _ _ _ _

3. To change or make different. It sounds like *altar*.

3. _ _ _ _ _

4. To fly very high. It sounds like *sore*.

4. _ _ _ _

5. A young swan. It sounds like *signet*.

5. _ _ _ _ _ _

6. The forward part of a ship. It sounds like *bough*.

6. _ _ _ _

7. A bird used for food. It sounds like *foul*.

7. _ _ _ _

8. A wreath of flowers. It sounds like *lay*.

8. _ _ _

9. A deed showing great courage or strength. It sounds like *feet*.

9. _ _ _ _

10. A kind of African antelope. It sounds like *knew*.

10. _ _ _

Asking for Information

Letters written to companies, organizations, or businesspeople are called **business letters**. Use a business letter to ask for information or order something from a company. Here are some points to keep in mind when writing a business letter.

1 Write neatly in ink or type on plain paper.

2 Make sure the margins are equal. Frame your letter like a picture.

3 Write on only one side of the paper.

4 Be brief and to the point. Businesspeople are busy.

5 If you type your letter, double space between paragraphs and type your name under the signature.

Study the following example to learn how business letters are organized.

Heading
(Your address
and the date)

1094 West 48th Avenue
Vancouver, B.C.
V6M 2N7
May 2, 1989

Inside Address
(Name and
address of the
receiver)

Director of Summer Recreation Programs
Public Utilities Commission
Box 2700
London, Ontario
N6A 4H6

Salutation
(followed by a
colon)

Dear Sir/Madam:

Body
(Remember the
5 C's. Be clear,
concise, correct,
complete, and
courteous)

During July I'll be visiting my aunt who lives in London. As she works each morning, I'll be on my own and would like to get involved with young people my own age. My aunt suggested that I contact you to see what programs you have planned for the summer.

I am thirteen years old and very interested in both sports and music. During the past year, I played on a number of school teams and particularly enjoyed baseball and soccer. For the last three years I've taken trumpet lessons and would really enjoy playing in a band with people my own age. Recently my parents gave me a camera for my birthday, so I'd enjoy a beginner's photography class.

If you'll be offering any programs you think I'd enjoy, please send me information on how to become involved.

Thank you very much for your help. I'm really looking forward to spending July in your city.

**Complimentary
Closing**
(Line up with
the date, use a
comma,
capitalize the
first word)

Yours truly,

Brian Sims

Brian Sims

Signature
(Sign your name
clearly)

B. Using this letter as a model, write a letter to a summer camp director to ask about the camp's program and facilities. In your letter, outline your background and some of your interests.

Checking Up on Capital Letters

C. Use the proofreading symbol for capitalization to show which letters in the following sentences need capitals.

1. there are many chinese restaurants on east pender street in vancouver.

2. last summer my sister caught the german measles.

3. the native people who live on the queen charlotte islands off the west coast of british columbia are known as the haida.

4. on june 15 colonel dempster opened the montgomery street bridge across the willow river.

5. next winter my sister will be teaching geography and german at the university of saskatchewan in saskatoon.

6. my grandfather told me many interesting stories about my mother and my aunt charlene.

7. the rotary club meets every second tuesday at eagle ridge school on falcon crescent.

8. last christmas, aunt sylvia gave my father a subscription to a magazine called *canadian geographic*.

9. drive south on fifty-third street until you reach the commodore hotel.

10. helgoland, an island in the north sea, belongs to west germany.

Reviewing Editing Skills

During the winter, many Canadians enjoy cross-country and downhill skiing. Skiing probably began in Scandinavia, in northern Europe. Here is a report on skiing in Norway, a country in Scandinavia. As you read the following paragraphs, think about how you could improve them.

Norwegians have always enjoyed skiing. Archaeologists have found cave drawings showing Stone Age hunters on skis. These carvings were found in a cave on the island of Rodoy. Rodoy is an island off the west coast of Norway. It is just south of the Arctic Circle. These drawings were discovered in 1927. People have found more than a hundred very old skis in good condition. These skis were buried in peat bogs. The oldest were about 4500 years old.

In ancient times people didn't ski for fun. Skis were used to help people get from place to place. Hunters used skis when they looked for reindeer and elk. Warriors used skis in

battle. Doctors used skis to visit the sick. Mail carriers used skis to make their rounds.

Skis have changed over the years. Today skiers use a pair of matched skis. Early skiers used two different kinds of ski. One was long and made of hard wood. It was smooth and was used for gliding. The other ski was short. It was covered with animal skin. It was used for pushing. Early cross-country skis were as wide as twenty-five centimetres. Now cross-country skis are much narrower. They are not more than six centimetres wide. Long ago, bindings were just single toe straps. They were made of willow or leather thongs.

Just over a hundred years ago, people who lived in Telemark made skiing into a sport. Telemark is in south-central Norway. They began shaping and tapering their skis. They also developed heel and toe straps for skis. The first timed ski race was held in Telemark. This race took place in 1848. The winner covered the five-kilometre course in just under thirty minutes.

1. If you were to edit these paragraphs, what changes would you make? Try to think of at least three changes.

_____

_____

_____

2. Now edit the paragraphs making the following changes.
   a. Join sentences wherever you can. Don't just put sentences together with *and*. Before you start, review the suggestions for combining sentences in Unit 16.
   b. Avoid using the same subject to start sentences that follow each other.
   c. Improve the topic sentences so they will catch the reader's attention.

Unit 23

Understanding Prepositions

A **preposition** is a word that shows the relationship between a pronoun or noun and another word. Let's look at some examples.

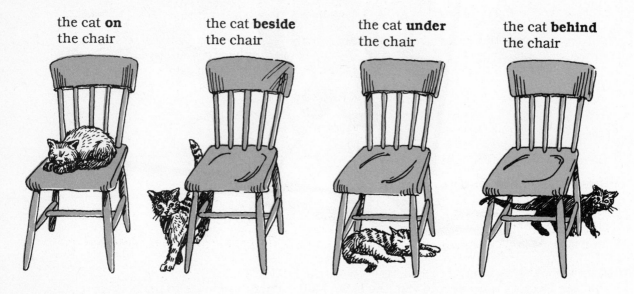

the cat **on** the chair

the cat **beside** the chair

the cat **under** the chair

the cat **behind** the chair

The words *on*, *beside*, *under*, and *behind* are prepositions. Each of these prepositions shows where the cat is in relation to the chair.

These are some of the most common prepositions:

about	around	between	in	out	toward
above	at	beyond	into	outside	under
across	before	by	near	over	until
after	behind	down	of	past	up
against	below	during	off	since	upon
along	beneath	for	on	through	with
among	beside	from	onto	to	without

A group of words that begins with a preposition and ends with a noun or a pronoun is called a **prepositional phrase**. In the sentence, *The man in the blue overalls raced up the stairs*, the words *in the blue overalls* and *up the stairs* are prepositional phrases.

Prepositional phrases end with either a noun or a pronoun, which is called the **object of the preposition**. This word usually answers the question "What?" or "Who?"

The table *beside the door* is an antique.

(The noun "door" tells *what* the table is beside.)

The team from Swift Current left *before us*.

(The pronoun "us" tells *who* the team left before.)

A. Circle the prepositions in the following sentences, draw an arrow from the preposition to the noun or pronoun that is its object, and underline the prepositional phrase or phrases. The number in parentheses at the end of each sentence tells how many prepositional phrases you should find.

Example:

The detective didn't look under the bed. (1)

1. The sign on the old building faded during the summer. (2)

2. My father just bought the hotel on Selkirk Avenue. (1)

3. Across the road and into the bushes scurried the three young foxes. (2)

4. About noon, the house across the street caught fire. (2)

5. The boy beside me fainted during the experiment. (2)

6. On weekends, Lance works for Mr. Penrose. (2)

7. The strange creature with the bloodshot eyes oozed slowly toward us. (2)

8. Suddenly the tiger on the barrel lunged toward the trainer. (2)

9. The man in the brown jacket dashed down the alley and into the burning building. (3)

10. The horses in that corral are going to the Circle R Ranch near High River. (3)

Using Quotation Marks

When you *quote* someone, you tell what that person said. There are two ways of doing this. In a **direct quotation**, you use the person's exact words and quote them *directly*.

Paul said, "I don't agree with Karen."

At other times, you may simply report what was said. As you are not using the speaker's exact words, this is called an **indirect quotation**.

Paul said that he didn't agree with Karen.

Notice how the wording changes. *I* becomes *he* and *don't* becomes *didn't*.
Here are some rules for using quotation marks.

1 Quotation marks (" ") mark the beginning and end of direct quotations. They always come in pairs. Do not use quotation marks with indirect quotations.

2 To separate a direct quotation from the rest of the sentence, use a comma. If the quotation is at the beginning of the sentence, place the comma *inside* the second set of quotation marks.

"Put the box of scissors on the shelf," replied Ted.

3 If the quotation is at the end of the sentence, the comma goes *before* the first set of quotation marks.

After examining the map carefully, the captain replied, "Let's try to land on the beach on the east side of the island."

4 Direct quotations always start with a capital letter.

B. Decide who is the speaker in each of the following sentences. Underline the speaker's exact words, and then punctuate the sentences correctly. Use the proofreading symbol to mark letters requiring capitals.

Example:

<u>I think you should leave him alone</u>, replied Norah.

1. The game will be played at Winskill Park replied the coach.

2. Perry said our team should have won the game.

3. I told you Connie was good at sports said Carolyn.

4. Howard thought for a minute and then said I think it's time you told your father.

5. I wouldn't leave your car unlocked warned the guard.

6. Better get to bed now said Mother.

7. Glancing nervously at the clock, Holly said I really think we should be leaving.

8. That's not the only thing that can happen to us whispered Charlie.

9. Quickly unlocking the door, Mr. Kreiger replied let's go.

10. You know perfectly well that camera is stolen said the detective.

C. In each of the following sentences, the writer has used an indirect quotation. Rewrite each sentence using a direct quotation. Be sure to punctuate your sentences correctly.

Example:

The librarian asked us to please talk more quietly.

The librarian said, "Please talk more quietly."

1. Mrs. Miller said she had been home all afternoon.

_____

2. Sharon suggested we leave right away.

_____

3. The boys promised they would be here by seven o'clock.

_____

4. Cheryl said she was going home.

_____

5. Hugh told me I could come with him.

_____

6. She replied that she'd be ready in a minute.

_____

7. Rebecca said she wouldn't be ready to leave before noon.

_____

8. The principal told us not to pay any attention to them.

_____

Planning with Outlines

A plan for a piece of writing is called an **outline**. An outline makes report writing much easier. It shows the major points you plan to cover and the order in which you will present them. Outlining is important because it helps you organize your thoughts in a logical order.

Once you've collected information on your topic, select the most important ideas you want to discuss. These ideas are the **main topics**. Decide on the best order for your main ideas and number them with Roman numerals. Then list the details that belong with each main idea under a suitable heading. These details are called **subtopics**. Precede each subtopic with a capital letter. You must have at least two subtopics under each main topic because whenever you divide something you must have at least two parts.

Outlines can be organized in different ways. Some writers use full sentences to plan their ideas. This kind of outline is called a **sentence outline**. Others find a **topic outline** easier to work with. A topic outline uses key phrases but not complete sentences. All the unimportant words are left out.

Let's look at a sample of a topic outline.

THE SKIN

   I. Layers of the Skin

      A. The Epidermis
         1. Thin outer layer
         2. Protects body from injury

      B. The Dermis
         1. Inner layer
         2. Much thicker than epidermis
         3. Contains blood vessels, nerves, and glands

  II. Purposes of the Skin

      A. Protection
         1. Keeps germs out
         2. Prevents water loss
         3. Shields from harmful rays of sun
         4. Completely waterproof

      B. Controls Body Temperature
         1. Sweat glands release heat
         2. Capillaries near skin surface give off heat

Use these questions to check your outline.

1. Does each main heading begin with a Roman numeral?
2. Have you put a period after each number and letter?
3. Have you capitalized the first word of each main idea?
4. Does the first word of each of the supporting details have a capital?
5. Are the numbers, letters, and periods in line vertically?

D. Farley Mowat, one of Canada's best-known writers, began his career at age thirteen by writing a weekly nature column called "Prairie Pals" for a Saskatoon newspaper. Here is some further information about Mowat. Arrange these details in a topic outline. Because these facts tell about a person's life, list them in time or chronological order. Use the plan at the end of the list.

- has written five books for children
- moved to Saskatoon with family at age 12
- served in World War II from 1940 to 1945
- books translated into thirty languages
- entered army as a private, left as a captain
- spent his first nine years in Trenton, Ontario
- first book, *People of the Deer*, published in 1952
- born in Belleville, Ontario, in 1921
- sent to England in October 1942
- family moved often when Mowat young
- has published over 300 magazine stories and articles
- spent much time in library as a child
- took part in the invasion of Italy in 1943

I. Early Life and Education

A. _____

B. _____

C. _____

D. _____

E. _____

II. Career in the Military

A. _____

B. _____

C. _____

D. _____

III. Career as a Writer

A. _____

B. _____

C. _____

D. _____

E. Suppose you are to write a report on comets. You'll find some useful information in the list below. As you read, look for details that belong together and sort them into five groups. Decide on a main idea for each group, and put these main ideas in an order that makes sense. Finally, make an outline for a report on comets in your notebook.

- comets are small, roughly one to ten kilometres in diameter
- most comets develop tails when close to the sun
- move in orbits around the sun
- for years people thought comets caused disasters
- centre of comet called nucleus
- hazy cloud called a coma surrounds nucleus
- Halley's comet reappears every 76 to 79 years
- some wore charms to protect from comet's evil powers
- tail always points away from the sun
- comets travel in an egg-shaped orbit
- nucleus contains frozen gases and water mixed with dust
- tail may be more than 160 million kilometres long
- Halley's comet last seen from earth in 1986
- often called dirty snowballs
- some tails long, others short and stubby
- some thought comets caused war, floods, and famine
- Halley's comet first seen 240 B.C.
- tails can take different shapes
- some orbit sun in just over three years

Unit 24

Writing a Report

Sometimes you'll find that a topic requires more than one paragraph. When this happens, you need to write a group of related paragraphs called a **report**. A well-written report contains accurate facts or information about a particular subject. In many ways, writing a report is much the same as writing a paragraph. The report differs from the paragraph mainly in that it's longer.

Before you write a report, take time to organize your thoughts. Organizing involves sorting things out and putting items that belong together in the same place. Get into the habit of outlining before you write.

Kira's class has been studying the human body in science. Her teacher has asked the students to write a report on one of the body systems. The teacher explains that a report must have a beginning, a middle, and an end. Kira has decided to research the respiratory system. Respiration is the process of breathing.

Reports should start with an **introductory paragraph** that introduces the main idea and gives the reader a preview of where the report is going. This paragraph should also catch the reader's attention. One way to do this is by asking a thought-provoking question.

Here's some information Kira collected for her introductory paragraph on the respiratory system.

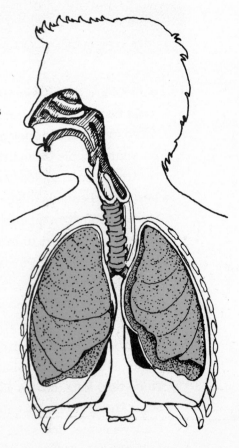

I. Introduction

   A. Respiration — taking in oxygen, giving off carbon dioxide

   B. People normally breathe fourteen to twenty times a minute

   C. Take about 600 million breaths in a lifetime

   D. Inhale almost four litres of air with each breath

   E. Lungs move enough air to blow up more than 1000 balloons each day

The middle section of the report is the longest part. Because these paragraphs develop and support the main idea of the report, they're called **developmental paragraphs**. Each developmental paragraph should deal with one part of the main idea. If you've taken time to prepare a well-thought-out outline, writing these paragraphs will be relatively easy.

Kira decided to write three developmental paragraphs. Here is the outline she made for her report.

II. Bringing Air Into the Body

   A. Air enters through the nose and the mouth

   B. Usually breathe only through the nose

   C. Breathe through mouth when extra air needed

   D. Hairs and mucus in the nose trap dirt

   E. Air moistened and warmed in the nose

   F. Moves to lungs through strong, flexible tube called trachea

   G. Trachea 1.5 cm in diameter, 10 cm in length

III. Inside Your Lungs

    A. Humans have two lungs

    B. Each lung about the size of an inflated football

    C. Lungs have many tiny air sacs called alveoli

    D. Each lung has 300 to 400 million alveoli

    E. Alveoli walls extremely thin

    F. Alveoli surrounded by tiny blood vessels called capillaries

    G. Oxygen and carbon dioxide pass through alveoli walls into capillaries

IV. Getting Air In and Out of the Lungs

    A. Strong curved muscle called diaphragm under lungs

    B. When you inhale, diaphragm flattens

    C. At same time, other muscles pull ribs outward

    D. Air pressure inside chest less than outside body

    E. Air pulled into the lungs

    F. When you exhale, diaphragm and chest muscles relax

    G. Chest space smaller, air forced out

A. Using the ideas in the introductory part of Kira's outline, write a short beginning paragraph in your notebook for a report on the respiratory system. Remember, this paragraph must explain what the report will be about *and* catch the reader's attention.

Now look over the rest of the information in her outline. Write topic sentences for each of the developmental paragraphs. Each topic sentence must tell clearly what the paragraph is about as well as keep the reader interested.

II. _____

   _____

III. _____

   _____

IV. _____

   _____

Using the topic sentences you've written and the information in Kira's outline, write the three developmental paragraphs in your notebook.

The concluding paragraph, like the introductory paragraph, should be brief. Its purpose is to bring the report to a smooth conclusion. Be careful in writing concluding paragraphs not to introduce any new ideas. Often the **concluding paragraph** is used to summarize the main ideas in the report.

Now write in your notebook a short concluding paragraph for this report.

Quotation Marks with Questions and Exclamations

When a quotation is a question or an exclamation, be sure to punctuate the sentence correctly. Study these examples carefully.

"Have you ever visited the Canadian Mint in Winnipeg?" asked Emily.

Emily asked, "Have you ever visited the Canadian Mint in Winnipeg?"

"Let's get out of here!" shouted the fire chief.

The fire chief shouted, "Let's get out of here!"

Notice that the question mark or exclamation mark:

1. Is always placed *inside* the final pair of quotation marks.

2. Takes the place of the comma if the quotation begins the sentence.

B. Rewrite these sentences in your notebook, punctuating them correctly.

1. Where did you leave my suitcase asked Diane
2. Don't try to cross that bridge warned the truck driver
3. Sit down before I lose my temper he roared
4. Will we ever see you again said the girls
5. The captain studied the map carefully and then asked how much fuel do we have left
6. Stay off the field bellowed the coach
7. Has anyone seen a blue raincoat asked the principal
8. I won't do it shouted Meg angrily stomping out of the room
9. Opening the door a crack, the old man asked what do you want
10. What took you so long inquired Mrs. Khan
11. Come down at once ordered the park ranger
12. Why do we have to stay out of sight whispered Christy

C. Rewrite each of the following sentences using a direct quotation. Be sure to punctuate each sentence correctly.

Example:

Mr. Parker asked us if we would like apple pie for dessert.

Mr. Parker asked, "Would you like apple pie for dessert?"

1. Ellen said that she'd be leaving in fifteen minutes.

_____

2. The park ranger asked if we had a pair of binoculars.

_____

3. Carl said that he didn't know how to ride a horse.

_____

4. The rancher shouted at us to stay away from that horse.

_____

5. Willy asked if we could give him a ride home.

_____

6. Giles insisted that I could not come with him.

_____

7. The coach asked Julie if she had ever played second base.

_____

8. Rebecca asked if she could borrow my red pen.

_____

Combining Sentences with Prepositional Phrases

Often you can use prepositional phrases to combine a number of short sentences. Let's look at an example:

> The detective carefully searched the beach.
>
> He had a metal detector.
>
> He was looking for the missing key.
>
> The detective with the metal detector carefully searched the beach for the missing key.

D. In each of the following groups of sentences, use the first sentence as a base. Change the other two sentences into prepositional phrases and combine them with the first sentence.

1. The old man trudged along the road.

   He wore a yellow raincoat.

   He was accompanied by his small dog.

_____

_____

2. My mother takes trumpet lessons.

   Her lessons are on Monday afternoon.

   Ms.Taninaka is her teacher.

_____

_____

3. Last week I found a wristwatch.

It had a brown strap.

I found it near the shopping centre.

_____

_____

Using Pronouns with Prepositions

In Unit 15 you learned that the object form of a pronoun (*me, him, her, it, us, you,* and *them*) must follow an action verb.

The dog bit **him** on the leg.

The object form of a pronoun must also be used after a preposition.

Let's go skiing with **them** this afternoon.

Take extra care when the object of a preposition includes a noun *and* a pronoun. The pronouns are used correctly in the following examples.

Mr. Taylor gave the baseball cards to Lorne and *him.*

The horse threw Helen and *me* into the river.

E. Some of the following sentences need subject pronouns. Others need object pronouns. Write the correct pronoun in the blank at the right. Test each sentence by reading it without the noun and the word *and.*

Example:

Are you speaking to George and (I, me)?   *me* _____

1. The boys left without Mike and (he, him).   1. _____

2. The dog splashed water on Mrs. Burns and (we, us).   2. _____

3. Pass those boxes to Sheila and (I, me).   3. _____

4. Last week Bernie and (I, me) flew to Yellowknife.   4. _____

5. The coach asked Norah and (she, her) to play.   5. _____

6. Why don't you come with Becky and (I, me)?   6. _____

7. As always, Glenna and (she, her) arrived early.   7. _____

8. The decorations for the party were made by Marty and (he, him).   8. _____

9. Noreen came with Mary Ann and (I, me).   9. _____

10. When Mario comes, (he, him) and (I, me) are going swimming.   10. _____

Using Similes to Compare

We often use comparisons to clarify our meaning. Suppose you're writing a story in which someone suddenly grabs the main character. You could say, "Suddenly a shadowy figure grabbed my arm." Now let's look at another way to express the same idea.

Suddenly a shadowy figure gripped my arm with fingers as strong as an eagle's talons.

In this sentence, the writer uses a comparison to help the reader more clearly imagine what happened. Comparisons made by using the words *like* or *as* are called **similes**. The word "simile" is from the Latin word *similis* meaning "like." The word "similar" is from the same Latin root. A simile points out a likeness between two different objects or ideas.

Care must be taken when using similes. For example, a comparison that is made repeatedly soon loses its effect. Overused similes are called **clichés**. Expressions such as *as black as night*, *as easy as pie*, and *as quick as a wink* are clichés. Be careful not to use these phrases in your writing.

F. Complete the following sentences with interesting similes of your own. Be careful not to use clichés.

1. The baby's skin was as soft as _____

   _____

2. When the giant yawned, his mouth looked like _____

   _____

3. The hungry shark rushed toward the injured diver like _____

   _____

4. In the moonlight, the snow glistened like _____

   _____

5. When everyone had left, I felt as lonesome as _____

   _____

6. The monkey grabbed the banana as quickly as _____

   _____

7. The hawk soared across the sky like _____

   _____

8. The old man's face was as wrinkled as _____

   _____

9. From the mountaintop the lake looked like _____

   _____

Unit 25

Write Your Own Myth

People have enjoyed telling and listening to stories for thousands of years. Storytelling probably began around the world's first campfires. After a day's hunting, people would often relax and talk about their adventures.

The ancient Greeks loved to tell stories. Many of their tales were about gods and heroes who lived in supernatural worlds. Today these stories are called **myths**. Myths were often invented to explain a happening in nature.

The mightiest of the Greek heroes was Heracles, the son of Alcmene and Zeus, king of the gods. (The Romans told stories about a similar strongman, called Hercules.) Heracles first showed his strength at ten months of age. Two huge poisonous snakes crept into the nursery where he and his twin brother slept. Grabbing one of the serpents in each hand, Heracles quickly strangled them!

When he grew up, Heracles soon became the best in Greece at archery, boxing, and wrestling. But Hera, the wife of Zeus, hated Heracles and was jealous of Alcmene, his mother. One day, Hera drove him into a fit of madness. Not knowing what he was doing, Heracles killed his wife, Megara, and their two sons.

As punishment, he had to serve his cousin, King Eurystheus (*you RIS thee us*), for twelve years. Each year the king ordered him to perform a very dangerous and difficult task or labor. These assignments led Heracles to battle fierce lions, ferocious bulls, and deadly multiheaded water snakes.

Suppose you were going to write a story about one of Heracles' labors. Before writing, you would take time to think about the order of events in your story. This kind of plan is called a **plot**. Organizing a story's plot is much like preparing an outline for a report.

Like reports, stories usually have a beginning, a middle, and an end. The beginning introduces the main characters and explains where, and when, the story takes place. The writer often describes what the main character wants, and what is preventing him or her from reaching this goal.

The beginning of your story should grab the reader's interest. For an action-packed tale, such as the story of Heracles, you might start with an attention-getting sentence. William Nolan, for example, began one of his short stories with the line, "Len had been dead for a month when the phone rang."

Another technique — describing where the story takes place — can arouse the reader's curiosity. Here is how Arthur C. Clarke began his short story entitled "Who's There?"

> The space suit — a miniature space ship shaped like a tubby cylinder — gave its occupants a superb view of the heavenly bodies. But the only sounds that ought to have been audible were those of the faint whirr of fans and motors or the gentle hiss of oxygen. But though every dial showed normal, there was another sound. Something was horribly wrong.

Starting your story with an interesting conversation between the main character and another person is also an effective way to begin.

A. Imagine Heracles has been summoned to the king's palace to learn about his sixth labor. King Eurystheus demands he capture a large flock of birds living in the Stymphalian Marsh. These enormous birds have claws and beaks of solid brass which can cut through the strongest shield. They also have sharp feathers that they can shoot like arrows. They feed on lambs and small calves and are especially fond of eating people.

1. What do you think Heracles and Eurystheus would talk about during their meeting? (The men dislike each other intensely. In fact, Eurystheus secretly wishes that Heracles would die on one of his assignments.)

   Write their conversation, or dialogue, in your notebook. Remember, this conversation must catch your reader's interest and make Heracles' problem clear. Don't allow one character to talk too long without a break, or your reader may lose interest.

   Be sure to start a new paragraph each time the speaker changes. If a quotation is made up of several sentences, put one set of quotation marks at the beginning of the first sentence. The second set belongs at the end of the last sentence. Once you've written your dialogue, read it aloud to make sure it sounds natural.

   The middle section of a story tells how the main character struggles to overcome his or her problem. This section, however, is more than just a series of adventures. In an *effective* plot, each incident grows out of the one before and leads into the one that follows.

   Remember that Heracles is extremely powerful. To keep the reader's interest, you should highlight his struggles against tremendous odds. If the battle is too one-sided, your reader may soon lose interest.

   Heracles' first problem is to locate the birds that live among the rocks and thick reeds of the Stymphalian Marsh. Finding their hiding places will be difficult. The marsh is full of quicksand that swallows anything that ventures in. Thousands of bones from previous victims litter the shore.

2. Imagine you're Heracles looking out over the marsh. Write six specific adjectives you could use to describe the scene.

   _____

   Hundreds of deadly water snakes share the marsh with the birds. How can Heracles avoid being bitten by these snakes as he searches for the birds?

   _____

   _____

How might Heracles find the birds? List the steps in your plan on the following lines.

_____

_____

_____

_____

Heracles' next problem is to find how he can capture the birds without being injured himself.
He cannot use poison, as water from the marsh runs into streams from which many animals
drink. No one has ever been able to shoot an arrow, or throw a spear with enough force, to
hurt them.

3. If you were Heracles, how would you go about getting rid of these birds? List the steps in
your plan on the following lines.

_____

_____

_____

_____

_____

Good endings are just as important as good beginnings. The most exciting part of a story is
the **climax**, the highest point of action or interest in the story. By this point the hero must
overcome all difficulties and solve the problem.

4. Plan the climax of your story. How will Heracles finally solve the problem of the Stymphalian
birds?

_____

_____

_____

Once the main character's problem is solved, your story is over. Following the climax, you
could wind up your story by revealing the main character's feelings about what has
happened.

5. Imagine Heracles is trudging back to King Eurystheus with several of the birds slung over his
back. What might he be thinking?

_____

_____

6. Using your prepared outline, write the story of Heracles' sixth labor in your notebook.

B. Imagine you could assign Heracles, or some other powerful person, a difficult task. Write a
story explaining what you would ask this person to do and how he or she would go about it.

Punctuating Split Quotations

Usually expressions such as "he said" come at the beginning or the end of a sentence. Sometimes, however, they are placed in the middle, as in the following example.

"I think," said Charles, "that I'll buy that jacket."

Sentences like this need two pairs of quotation marks. Notice that only the first word in the quotation has a capital letter. Pay close attention to where the commas are placed.

C. Punctuate the following sentences correctly. Use the proofreading symbol to mark letters requiring capitals.

1. The four horses down by the stream said the rancher are Arabians

2. The hardest part of learning to swim explained the instructor is getting your arms and legs to work together

3. Don't cross that bridge yelled the truck driver

4. Why whispered Chris do we have to keep our heads down

5. What if something terrible has already happened replied Miss Ito

6. Well said Suman what did you have in mind

7. Sit down he roared before I lose my temper

8. Will we ever see you again asked the girls

9. Just when asked the officer is he expected to return

10. Why begged Justin can't Brent and I go with you

D. Write interesting sentences in your notebook following these directions.

1. A sentence containing a direct quotation and starting with "Finally the lifeguard asked."

2. A sentence containing a direct quotation and ending with "the coach bellowed."

3. A sentence containing a direct quotation interrupted with "suggested Mr. Devitt."

4. A sentence containing a direct quotation ending with "demanded the wrestler in the purple trunks."

5. A sentence containing a direct quotation ending with "shouted the officer."

6. A sentence containing a direct quotation starting with "After listening to my explanation my father asked."

7. A sentence containing a direct quotation interrupted with "thundered the giant."

Using Phrases to Make Nouns More Exact

Prepositional phrases often give the reader important details. Suppose, for example, you witnessed a hit-and-run accident in which a young girl was injured by a cyclist. Telling the police that the girl was hit by a person on a bicycle would not be too helpful. Notice how exact the report becomes when phrases are added.

A man *with curly black hair* riding a bicycle *from Budget Rentals* struck the girl.

Because the phrases in italics tell us about the nouns "man" and "bicycle," they are called **adjective phrases**. Adjective phrases describe nouns in the same way that single adjectives do.

E. Underline the adjective phrase in each of the following sentences. Draw an arrow from the phrase to the noun each modifies or describes.

Example:

In August we visited the lighthouse at Cape Forchu.

1. The bridge across Bryce Canyon collapsed last night.

2. The two benches along that trail should be replaced.

3. The sports car with the flat tire is my uncle's.

4. The driver behind us started honking his horn.

F. In the following sentences, blanks have been left after some of the nouns. Fill in each of these blanks with an adjective phrase. Make sure each phrase starts with a preposition and ends with a noun or a pronoun. Try to use as many different prepositions as possible.

Example:

At noon, the secretary ____*with the red hair*____ hurriedly left the building.

1. Last week the new house _____ was sold to a family _____ .

2. The waiter _____ is a drummer in a rock band.

3. In the cupboard _____ the detective found a strange box _____ .

4. The cake _____ is delicious.

5. Within minutes the heron had eaten all the goldfish _____ .

6. After the game, the team _____ went out for pizzas.

7. The girl _____ won first prize in the pie-eating contest.

8. The man _____ did not stop at the traffic light _____ .

Unit 26

Using Prepositional Phrases to Explain Where, When, and How

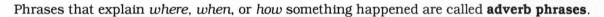

Prepositional phrases give more information about verbs, just as adverbs do. For example:

>The squirrel sat *on the rock* to eat the nut.

>(The phrase *on the rock* tells *where* the squirrel ate the nut.)

>Squirrels are especially busy *in the autumn*.

>(The phrase *in the autumn* tells *when* the squirrels are busy.)

>The coyote grabbed the squirrel *in its jaws*.

>(The phrase *in its jaws* tells *how* the coyote grabbed the squirrel.)

Phrases that explain *where*, *when*, or *how* something happened are called **adverb phrases**.

A. Underline the adverb phrase in each of the following sentences. On the line under each sentence, write the phrase and explain what it does in the sentence.

>**Example**:

>The lunar module landed <u>near the crater</u>.

>*near the crater – tells where the module landed*

1. With lightning speed the mongoose attacked the cobra.

   _____

2. Mountain lions usually hunt at night.

   _____

3. The rescue helicopter lifted the injured hiker from the canyon.

   _____

4. Across the still water floated the haunting call of the loon.

   _____

5. My younger sister can run like a deer.

   _____

6. Last night the wolves began howling about ten o'clock.

   _____

7. Put the bag of fertilizer in the shed.

   _____

B. Fill in the blanks in the following sentences with adverb phrases. Be sure to follow the directions in parentheses.

1. On Monday our class spent the day _____

_____ . (where)

2. The team travelled to the game _____

_____ . (how)

3. Mark and Stan left the concert _____

_____ . (when)

4. When the coyote appeared the ground squirrels scampered _____

_____ . (where)

5. _____ (when)

my brother takes karate lessons.

6. _____ (how)

the rhinoceros charged toward us.

Punctuating Titles

1 Use quotation marks around the title of a poem, short story, short play, article, song, or chapter in a book:

> Last week our teacher read the poem "The Highwayman."
>
> The science test next week is on the chapter entitled "Understanding Energy."

2 Underline the titles of books, magazines, newspapers, full-length plays, movies, and television shows. In typeset materials, titles are italicized.

> We read about the aircraft hijacking in <u>The Globe and Mail</u>.
>
> The musical <u>Anne of Green Gables</u> is performed every summer at the Confederation Centre of the Arts in Charlottetown.

C. In the following sentences use the proofreading symbols to mark the letters that should be capitalized and insert the correct punctuation.

1. mr brady asked us to memorize the first two stanzas of robert services poem the shooting of dan mcgrew for next tuesday

2. the audience sang o canada at the beginning of the program

3. my favorite short stories are the necklace all summer in a day and the fun they had

4. did you read the chapter beginning on page eleven entitled skin the bag you live in

5. pierre bertons books the national dream and the last spike will give you much information on the building of the canadian pacific railway

6. the february 1988 edition of national geographic contains several articles on australia

7. in 1988 the movie the last emperor won nine academy awards

8. before writing your report on logging in british columbia be sure to read the article entitled the last stand in the february march 1986 issue of canadian geographic

Troublesome Words

A few words in English cause a lot of trouble. When you proofread your work, pay close attention to the words on this list.

1. **a lot** Always write *a lot* as two words.

   My grandparents have **a lot** of antiques.

2. **all together/altogether** The phrase *all together* means "together in a group." The adverb *altogether* means "all included, completely, or entirely."

   We found the cows **all together** down by the stream.

   Altogether there are ten books in the series.

   He wasn't **altogether** surprised.

3. **accept/except** To *accept* means "to receive" or "to agree to." *Except* usually means "not including" or "but."

   Are you sure Ms. Brady will still **accept** your assignment?

   All the boys **except** Nelson have their uniforms.

4. **advice/advise** *Advice* is a noun meaning "suggestions." *Advise* is a verb meaning "to give advice or information."

   Why did you not follow the doctor's **advice**?

   Which computer would you **advise** me to buy?

5. **between/among** Use *between* when you are talking about *two* persons or objects. Use *among* when you are talking about *more than two* persons or objects.

   Stretch the rope **between** the two fir trees.

   Divide the cake **among** the five boys.

6. **affect/effect** *Affect* is a verb meaning "to make something happen to" or "to have an effect on." *Effect* is usually used as a noun meaning "something that happens as a result of something else."

   The lack of rain will **affect** the crops this year.

   What **effect** did the medicine have on your grandmother?

7. **learn/teach** To *learn* is to gain knowledge or skill. To *teach* is to communicate knowledge or skills to others.

Last summer I **learned** how to develop black and white film.

Mrs.Burns **teaches** French at Maple Grove School.

8. **loose/lose** *Loose* means "not firmly tied or fastened." *Lose* means to mislay or to part with by accident.

My younger sister has a **loose** tooth.

Where did you **lose** your keys?

9. **quiet/quite** The word *quiet* has two syllables (qui-et). It means "still" or "making no sound." *Quite* is a one-syllable word meaning "completely, wholly, really."

Keep **quiet** and listen!

Are you **quite** sure you want to leave?

10. **than/then** *Than* is used to compared people or things. *Then* means "next" or "at that time."

Athena runs faster **than** her brother.

Then we decided to go swimming.

D. Twelve of the following sentences contain an error. Cross out the incorrect word and write your correction on the blank at the right. Write the word "correct" in the blank following the three sentences that don't have errors.

1. Where did you loose your watch?

1. _____

2. The books on the space shuttle are altogether on the shelf under the window.

2. _____

3. I am faster than Sumanjit.

3. _____

4. Will you learn me how to play chess?

4. _____

5. Are you quite sure you don't have your wallet?

5. _____

6. What would you advice me to do now?

6. _____

7. Everyone arrived on time accept Geoff.

7. _____

8. Put the glasses all together in the cupboard.

8. _____

9. The affect of too much reading often is sore eyes.

9. _____

10. I still have alot of work to do on my report.

10. _____

11. Divide the chocolates equally between the three boys.

11. _____

12. That wheel has four lose spokes.

12. _____

13. If Barbara broke the window, than she should pay for it.

13. _____

14. Will your mother except that excuse?

14. _____

15. Are you quiet sure you're not hurt?

15. _____

E. In your notebook, use ten words from the list of "Troublesome Words" in interesting sentences. You may use more than one of the words in a sentence.

How Will This Adventure End?

Just before dawn on the first Saturday in April, Connie slipped quietly out of her room and tiptoed downstairs to the kitchen. Fifteen minutes later, she had finished breakfast, slipped a chocolate bar into her jacket pocket, picked up her camera, and headed outside. The sky was still overcast, but the weather forecast was for sunny periods later in the day.

Eager to begin the day's activities, her dog Shep greeted her enthusiastically. Connie quickly got the dog under control. If her parents knew what she was going to do, they would certainly not allow her to go. For some time she had secretly planned to hike to Hamilton Lake near the top of Mount Seymour. No need to leave a note, she thought. If everything went as planned, she'd be home by noon.

After walking for two hours, Connie noticed a small stream heading off to the left and decided to follow it. Some distance from the main trail, she paused. In the canyon far below, she heard the roar of a large waterfall. Determined to reach it, she headed farther downstream, forcing her way through the thick underbrush.

Thirty minutes later she got her first glimpse of the waterfall. The best pictures, she decided, would be from high up on the rocky ridge to the right. The route to the top was difficult, but Connie persisted and after an hour of struggling finally reached the top.

Suddenly she realized that the weather had turned much colder. A few flakes of snow had started to fall and a cold north wind swept across the ridge. Connie had learned about the dangers of hypothermia, or loss of body heat, in school. She realized she didn't have long to get back.

As she hurried down from the ridge, the snow began to fall more heavily. Within minutes, Connie could see only a few metres ahead. By the time she reached the forest, she realized she was lost. Why hadn't she brought the emergency kit she had learned about in her wilderness survival classes at school? Why hadn't she worn her hiking boots instead of running shoes? Checking her jacket pockets, Connie found nothing but the chocolate bar.

As the icy wind began whipping the snow into drifts, Connie huddled under a large evergreen with Shep and tried to decide what to do. Sending the dog home with a message was out of the question. Connie had had Shep for only a few weeks. Not long enough, unfortunately, to teach him important skills such as going for help. She also realized that no one knew where she was.

F. Use your imagination to put yourself in Connie's place. What could she do to get out of this situation? How could she keep warm? In what ways might the dog help? How might her parents become involved? How might she finally be rescued?

Finish this story in your notebook. Before you start writing, take time to plan the plot carefully. List the events leading up to the climax.

Unit 27

Editing a Report

People in dry climates have relied on camels for at least four thousand years. In fact, it's unlikely that humans could live in the deserts of Africa and Asia without the camel's help. These amazing beasts have carried people and supplies and have been used in wars. Even today, camels carry food and equipment through areas where powered vehicles cannot go.

A. Here is some additional information on the camel. As you read this report, think about how it could be improved.

Camels are well suited to life in the desert. Camels have broad feet. The toes on each foot are joined together by a fleshy pad. This pad spreads when the camel steps on it. Their feet are like snowshoes. Their feet keep them from sinking in the soft sand. Their feet also prevent them from slipping on rocks. Camels have long eyelashes. These eyelashes protect their eyes from the sand. Camels can close their nostrils. Sand can't blow into their noses.

Camels can go for a long time with little or no food and water. On the trail camels may have to live on dried leaves. Camels also eat most desert plants. If food is scarce, camels will eat almost anything. Even their owner's tent. Camels can go a long time without water. When they do find water, they can drink over one hundred litres in ten minutes.

People use camels for many purposes. Camels grow thick wool. This wool is soft. The wool can be spun into long threads. The wool can then be woven into fine cloth. It can also be used to make good rugs. A camel's hide makes good sandals. The hide is also used for water containers. Good saddles can be made from the hide, too.

Camels are an important source of food for many desert dwellers. People eat the meat of young camels. This meat tastes like veal. Camel's milk is good to drink. The milk is thick and rich. It is often used to make cheese.

1. If you were to edit this report, what changes would you make? Try to think of at least four ways to improve this piece of writing.

   a. _____

   b. _____

   c. _____

   d. _____

2. Now edit the report making the following changes.

   a. Join sentences wherever you can. Be creative! (Don't just put sentences together with *and*.) Before you start, review the suggestions for combining sentences in Unit 16.

   b. Try not to have sentences that follow each other start with the same subject.

   c. The four topic sentences in this report need improvement. Rewrite these sentences to catch the reader's attention.

   d. The word "camels" has been overused. When you rewrite, occasionally replace this word with a pronoun or a phrase such as "these animals."

   e. The general adjective "good" has been used too often in the third paragraph. Use a thesaurus to find specific synonyms to replace this word.

Homonym Problems

Always proofread your work carefully to catch homonym errors. Listed below are six word pairs that often cause trouble. Study them carefully.

1. **coarse/course** *Coarse* is an adjective meaning "rough" or "not fine." The noun *course* is "a series of lessons," "an area for a sport or a game," or "a part of a meal."

2. **complement/compliment** *Complement* means "something that makes complete." *My mother felt the gloves complemented her new fall outfit.* A *compliment* is an expression of praise.

3. **desert/dessert** Used as a noun, *desert* means "a dry land on which few plants grow." As a verb, it means "to run away from." *Dessert* is the final course of a meal, usually sweet.

4. **passed/past** *Passed* is the past tense of the verb *pass*, meaning "to move or go by," "to get through," or "to succeed at." *Erin passed her piano exam last week.* The word *past* means "time gone by." *In the past, people travelled by stagecoach. Past* is never used as a verb.

5. **principal/principle** The *principal* is the person who is in charge of a school or college. Sometimes the word "principal" is used as an adjective to mean "most important" or "main." *The principal crop raised on New Brunswick farms is potatoes.* A *principle* is an important law, rule, or belief.

6. **stationary/stationery** *Stationary* is an adjective meaning "standing still, not moving." *Stationery* is a noun meaning "writing materials such as paper, cards, and envelopes."

B. In the following exercise, nine words are misspelled. Cross out each one and write the correct spelling above it. Be ready to write these sentences from dictation.

1. The principal complemented me because I past the science test.

2. The restaurant near the golf coarse serves delicious deserts.

3. This town's population has been stationery for the past five years.

4. The scientists travelled to the Sahara Dessert to test the new sunscreen.

5. In the past, large herds of caribou past through this pass.

6. Soon after he desserted, the soldier bought some stationary in Grande Prairie.

7. My father complimented the chef on the magnificent seven course dinner.

Working with Compounds

Compounds are two words that come together to make one word. Words such as *lifeboat, handball, grasshopper,* and *tablecloth* are examples of compounds.

Many compounds, such as *water-ski* and *make-up,* are written with a hyphen between the two parts.

Some compounds, such as *first aid, post office, living room,* and *cash register* are written as two separate words.

C. Each of the following groups of words can be combined to form a compound. Some should be written as one word, others as a hyphenated word, and a few as two words. Write the words as you think they should be combined in the blanks. When you finish, check your answers in the dictionary. You may find that dictionaries don't always agree with each other.

1. finger + nail _____

2. baby + sit _____

3. star + fish _____

4. gift + wrap _____

5. down + hill _____

6. sales + tax _____

7. long + winded _____

8. lawn + mower _____

9. after + noon _____

10. stop + light _____

11. fairy + tale _____

12. face + off _____

13. water + front _____

14. great + uncle _____

Checking Up on Punctuation and Capitalization

D. Rewrite the following sentences in your notebook adding punctuation and capitalization wherever necessary.

1. are you sure asked heather that this bus goes to the museum

2. youre not leaving yet victor replied the principal

3. the smiths dog a german shepherd is very well trained

4. the bus drivers coats however were left in mrs oakes office

5. if theyre going to be ready by nine oclock theyll certainly have to hurry warned mrs stanley

6. on may 29 1953 edmund hilary a new zealander and tenzing norgay his sherpa guide became the first to reach the top of mount everest the worlds highest mountain

7. company halt thundered the sergeant major

8. the waitresses uniforms came from osaka japan

9. stay where you are yelled the fire chief

10. the receptionist said jack your next appointment is on tuesday november 14 at two oclock

11. why cant we get tickets for saturdays game asked walter

12. wolfgang mozart one of the worlds greatest composers was born on january 27 1756 in salzburg austria

13. do you know asked laurie if the snowploughs have cleared the drifts on the freeway

14. oxygen shouted the doctor as the patient suddenly turned pale

15. the words i misspell most often replied charlene are pneumonia separate mischievous and vacuum

16. youll soon discover that its difficult to change my fathers mind warned angie

17. shouldnt we find out whos coming suggested maria before we order the pizza

18. a rodents jaws are particularly good for gnawing said domenica because they can move up and down backward forward and sideways

19. did you know replied sharon that some octopuses are no larger than your fingernail

20. but why asked rolf did you have to be late today

Checking Up on Subject-Verb Agreement

E. Proofread the following sentences. In eighteen of them, the verb doesn't agree with the subject. Cross out the incorrect verbs and write the correct answer in the blank supplied. Write the word "Correct" in the blank supplied for the seven correct sentences. Be prepared to give reasons for your answers.

1. There's many totem poles in Vancouver's Stanley Park.

   1. _____

2. The old man and his seven dogs walks through the park every morning.

   2. _____

3. Neither the bread nor the cookies is baked yet.   3. _____

4. Most of the houses on this street are quite expensive.   4. _____

5. "Has anyone seen three white mice?" inquired Trudy.   5. _____

6. "Where's the key to these handcuffs?" demanded the prisoner.   6. _____

7. Each of these books have a missing page.   7. _____

8. Jody and Erica plans to enter their frog in the race.   8. _____

9. Neither the hammer nor the wrenches was put back in the drawer.

   9. _____

10. There's seven goldfish in that tank.   10. _____

11. Either Ted or his sisters have the key.   11. _____

12. A few of the teachers' cars was damaged in the earthquake.   12. _____

13. The first two chapters of the novel was exciting.   13. _____

14. Either you or Pauline have to be there.

14. _____

15. Neither Mr.Hegler nor his wife are wealthy.

15. _____

16. There was several rotten oranges in the box.

16. _____

17. Off Canada's west coast is the Queen Charlotte Islands.

17. _____

18. The bat's favorite food are insects.

18. _____

19. Neither of those cars have been washed.

19. _____

20. Not one of the boys has been late this month.

20. _____

21. I think there's only two ways to escape.

21. _____

22. Neither Alberta nor Saskatchewan have a seacoast.

22. _____

23. Either my parents or my brother is going to take me
to the hockey game.

23. _____

24. Not one of the sweaters was the right size.

24. _____

25. Have either Mr.Gagnon or his secretary arrived?

25. _____

Checking Up on Editing Skills

F. The following paragraphs need editing. Some of the sentences should be removed as they are off the topic. Others should be combined. You may also decided to change the order of some of the sentences. Try not to have sentences that follow each other begin with the same subject.

Look carefully at the verbs and adjectives, too. Use a thesaurus to help you find more specific words.

Preparing a good meal on the space shuttle takes about thirty minutes. First the chef takes the meal packages from storage. Then he or she attaches these packages to the work table. The work table is in the galley or kitchen. The galley has an oven. It also has hot and cold water outlets.

Many of the foods are dehydrated. All the water has been removed. They are packed in plastic containers. My brother often takes dehydrated food with him when he goes camping. Dehydrated foods are used to reduce the weight at lift-off. Some of the dehydrated foods used on the shuttle are cereals, vegetables, soups, spaghetti, and scrambled eggs. Before they can be used, water must be added to the packages. The water is made by the shuttle's fuel cells. The chef uses a hollow needle to add water to these containers. The needle is attached to the hot water outlet.

The chef puts food in the oven to warm. Then the chef gets out the food trays. The chef puts these trays on the dining table. The trays are held in place by magnets. Then the chef adds cold water to the dessert. The chef adds water to the beverages, too. Astronauts can choose from twenty different beverages. Some of the beverages are apple, orange, and grape juice. They can also choose tropical fruit punch or lemonade.

When the heated foods are ready, the astronauts gather around the table. They eat standing up. Suction cups on their boots keep them in place. Astronauts have a knife, fork, and spoon to eat with. They also have a pair of scissors. They use the scissors to cut open their food packages. They can season their food with mustard and mayonnaise. They can

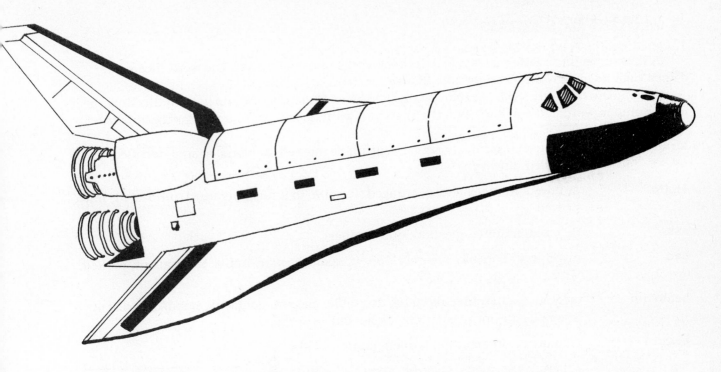

also use liquefied salt and pepper. Pepper is probably the most widely used spice in the world today. Astronauts must eat slowly. Sudden movements could make the food come loose. The food would then float around the cabin.

Food for space shuttle flights is carefully chosen. Foods must be easy to ingest. They must also be easy to digest. Foods are tested for taste and nutritional value. They are also tested for convenience in preparation. Food must also look good. Astronauts soon lose interest in eating if the food does not look nice.

Synonym Word Search

Hidden in this word search are thirty words that tell how animals or objects move. These words may be spelled backward or forward. They may be written vertically, horizontally, or diagonally. How many can you find?

```
C  E  T  R  U  D  G  E  Y  H  S  E
W  L  D  P  R  A  N  C  E  T  L  Z
K  F  I  I  C  S  R  U  R  K  I  O
H  F  E  M  R  H  P  E  O  E  D  O
H  U  C  L  B  T  A  T  T  B  E  D
U  H  X  W  D  K  S  G  O  N  A  P
S  S  K  L  A  W  S  H  C  R  A  M
T  H  D  S  N  A  A  T  T  N  T  C
L  S  O  C  D  D  M  D  R  E  L  R
E  U  L  O  L  D  A  S  C  O  L  A
B  R  P  O  T  L  O  A  P  Z  L  W
S  L  I  T  H  E  R  E  P  M  I  L
```

A Mini Thesaurus

A thesaurus (*thuh SAW rus*) is a collection of words and synonyms. The word thesaurus comes from a Greek word meaning "storehouse" or "treasure house."

A complete thesaurus will list thousands of entries. This mini thesaurus contains only the most common words. If you can't find the word you want, look it up in a regular thesaurus.

afraid   anxious, cowardly, horrified, fearful, frightened, nervous, scared, terrified, troubled, uneasy

angry   annoyed, aroused, cross, enraged, furious, in a rage, inflamed, infuriated, irate, peeved

ask   demand, inquire, question, quiz, request

bad   awful, evil, horrible, naughty, rotten, spoiled, unfavorable, unpleasant, wicked, wrong

beautiful   attractive, charming, dazzling, desirable, elegant, gorgeous, handsome, lovely, magnificent, pretty, sparkling, splendid, stunning

begin   commence, inaugurate, launch, start

big   colossal, enormous, gigantic, great, huge, immense, jumbo, large, mammoth, massive, titanic, vast

brave   bold, courageous, daring, fearless, gallant, heroic, unafraid, valiant

break   burst, crack, crush, damage, destroy, shatter, smash, split, wreck

bright   brilliant, colorful, dazzling, gleaming, glittering, glowing, shimmering, shiny, sparkling

call   bellow, cry, roar, scream, whisper, yell

catch   capture, grab, hook, rope, snare, snatch

cool   bitter, chilly, cold, freezing, frigid, frosty, ice-cold, icy, unheated, wintry

cry   bawl, bellow, exclaim, howl, roar, scream, shout, sob, wail, weep, yell

cut   carve, chop, clip, saw, slash, slice, snip

dark	black, dim, dismal, dreary, gloomy, murky, shadowy, sunless
delicious	appetizing, enjoyable, juicy, luscious, scrumptious, succulent, tasty

dirty	dingy, dusty, filthy, grimy, messy, smudged, soiled, unwashed
dull	boring, dreary, humdrum, tedious, tiring, uninteresting
eat	bite, chew up, crunch, devour, feast on, gobble, gnaw, graze, grind, gulp, munch, nibble, swallow
fall	collapse, dive, drop, plunge, sink, topple, tumble
fast	fleet, hasty, prompt, quick, rapid, speedy, swift
fat	chubby, obese, overweight, plump, pudgy, stout
full	crammed, crowded, heaping, jammed, loaded, overflowing, packed, stuffed
get	acquire, collect, earn, find, gather, obtain
good	agreeable, excellent, fine, first-rate, marvelous, pleasant, reliable, satisfactory, splendid, superb, superior, well-behaved, wonderful, trustworthy
happy	cheerful, contented, delighted, glad, jolly, joyful, jubilant, merry, overjoyed, pleased, satisfied
hate	abhor, despise, detest, disapprove, dislike, loathe
hit	collide, crash into, pound, punch, run into, slam into, smash into, strike
hot	baked, boiling, burning, fiery, roasting, scalded, scorched, sizzling, steaming, sunny, tropical, warm
hurry	accelerate, bustle, dash, dart, flash, hasten, hustle, race, run, rush, speed, zip, zoom
important	essential, famous, indispensable, influential, necessary, outstanding, prominent, significant, substantial, valuable, well-known
interesting	absorbing, appealing, amusing, arousing, attractive, engrossing, entertaining, enthralling, exciting, fascinating, gripping, intriguing, spellbinding, thrilling
kind	considerate, friendly, generous, gentle, helpful, pleasant, thoughtful, warm-hearted
little	dwarfish, miniature, minute, pigmy, small, tiny, wee
look	explore, gape, gawk, glance, glare, glimpse, hunt, inspect, observe, peek, peep, peer, search for, stare, study, watch

mad	angry, annoyed, cross, disagreeable, enraged, furious, raging
make	assemble, build, construct, create, develop, fashion, invent, manufacture, produce
move	amble, bound, climb, crawl, creep, dart, dash, gallop, hobble, jog, paddle, race, ride, run, rush, saunter, scamper, scramble, scurry, shuffle, slide, slither, stagger, streak, stride, swagger, tear, toddle, trot, waddle, walk
new	current, modern, recent, unused
old	aged, ancient, antique, elderly, feeble
right	accurate, correct, exact, perfect, true
sad	dejected, depressed, gloomy, miserable, sorrowful, sorry, unhappy
say	admit, announce, argue, assert, boast, chat, claim, comment, complain, continue, discuss, explain, express, grumble, growl, insist, mention, mumble, mutter, note, order, promise, recall, remark, reply, snap, suggest, thunder, urge, whisper, yell
show	demonstrate, disclose, explain, guide, point out, teach
slowly	gradually, lazily, leisurely, sluggishly, unhurriedly
smart	bright, brilliant, clever, intellectual, intelligent, wise
stop	block, cease, conclude, discontinue, end, halt, prevent
strange	astonishing, extraordinary, fantastic, odd, peculiar, queer, unusual, weird
strong	forceful, mighty, muscular, powerful, rugged, sturdy, tough
take	capture, carry off, grab, kidnap, obtain, pick up, seize, snap up, snatch
thin	lean, scrawny, skinny, slender, slim
true	accurate, actual, authentic, correct, exact, genuine, real, right
ugly	hideous, repulsive, unattractive, unsightly
unhappy	cheerless, dejected, depressed, discontented, discouraged, gloomy, heart-broken, miserable, sad, sorrowful
walk	file, hike, limp, march, pace, prance, stagger, stalk, stamp, stride, stroll, strut, stumble, tiptoe, trudge, waddle
wet	damp, drenched, humid, moist, rainy, soaked, soggy, sodden, watery
wonderful	amazing, delightful, enjoyable, fabulous, fantastic, marvelous, spectacular, superb
worried	agitated, anxious, concerned, disturbed, troubled, upset
wrong	false, inaccurate, incorrect, unsuitable, untrue